LABORATORY MANUAL OF
Structure and Function in Man

Second Edition

STANLEY W. JACOB, M.D., F.A.C.S.

Associate Professor of Surgery,
University of Oregon Medical School;
Lecturer in Anatomy,
University of Oregon School of Nursing;
Visiting Surgeon, University of Oregon
Medical School Hospitals and Clinics;
First Kemper Foundation Research Scholar,
American College of Surgeons;
Markle Scholar in Medical Sciences.

CLARICE ASHWORTH FRANCONE

Medical Illustrator,
Formerly Head of the Department of Medical Illustrations,
University of Oregon Medical School

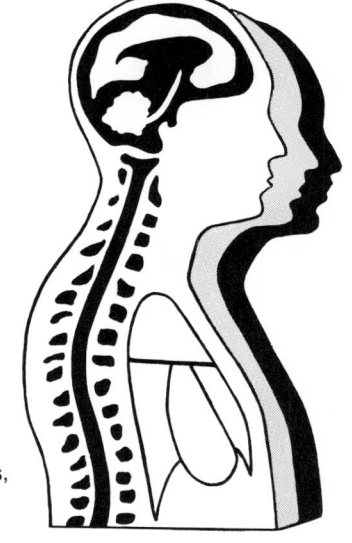

W. B. SAUNDERS COMPANY
PHILADELPHIA · LONDON · TORONTO

W. B. Saunders Company: West Washington Square
                          Philadelphia, Pa.   19105

                          12 Dyott Street
                          London, WC1A   1DB

                          833 Oxford Street
                          Toronto 18, Ontario

Laboratory Manual of Structure and Function in Man   ISBN 0-7216-5101-1

Print No.:   9   8   7   6

PREFACE TO SECOND EDITION

The second edition of this laboratory manual has undergone extensive revisions. Included are sections describing the methods of preparing solutions, an enlarged source list for materials to be used by the students, a film guide, and descriptive information on understanding medical terminology.

A number of new experiments have been added which include such exercises as RBC and WBC counting and studies on the histology of the ovary. New figures include, among others, the rib, fetal skull and histology of bone. More half-tone drawings have also been included. For clarity, study questions have been separated into two categories, those dealing with anatomy and physiology and those dealing with the clinical aspect of the particular subject under study.

It is hoped that this manual will permit the student to more effectively understand and correlate information on structure and function in man.

The contributions of many individuals are responsible for its revision. The authors would particularly like to express appreciation to Karen Clement, Beverly Chase, Stephen Jacob and Larry Stinson.

STANLEY W. JACOB
CLARICE A. FRANCONE

PREFACE TO FIRST EDITION

In the following laboratory exercises, the authors have utilized a variety of general approaches employed in modern biological research. These approaches should enable the student to study the structure and function of an animal part by scientific observation and manual manipulation, and so provide better correlation of function with structure.

The major reason for performing laboratory experiments is to make it possible for a student to become personally identified with the problems of a field by direct engagement in scientific approach and solution. A man working with his hands acquires an understanding that is far more rewarding than rote textbook memory.

The organization of this laboratory manual is similar to the text *Structure and Function in Man*. The directions to the student and instructor are explicit. Busy work has been excluded. The experiments have been constructed to enable the student to think, study, do research and draw independent conclusions. Practical exercises are included at the end of each chapter.

The contributions of many individuals are responsible for this manual. The authors would particularly like to express appreciation to Michael Davis, DeWayne Ditto, Larry Stinson and Frances Kemper.

It is expected that the student will look upon laboratory work as an opportunity to observe phenomena described in the text and lecture; as a chance to test the truth of the statements he has read; and as a means to gain knowledge of the factors involved in producing an end result; in summary, to actually see and study so that he might better comprehend the living, functioning animal body.

STANLEY W. JACOB
CLARICE A. FRANCONE

Portland, Oregon

SUGGESTIONS
TO STUDENTS

It is important that each student read the laboratory experiments to be performed and review lecture material pertinent to the experiments before coming to the laboratory. Always record collected data immediately after an experiment has been completed. Handle all laboratory materials carefully, and promptly report broken equipment. When the laboratory period is completed, put away all materials, wash glassware, clean desk top, and dispose of all used papers.

It is essential to understand that animals can feel pain. Since you would demand an anesthetic during a surgical operation, be certain that the experimental animal experiences no suffering or discomfort during dissection.

CONTENTS

SUGGESTED TIME ALLOTMENT

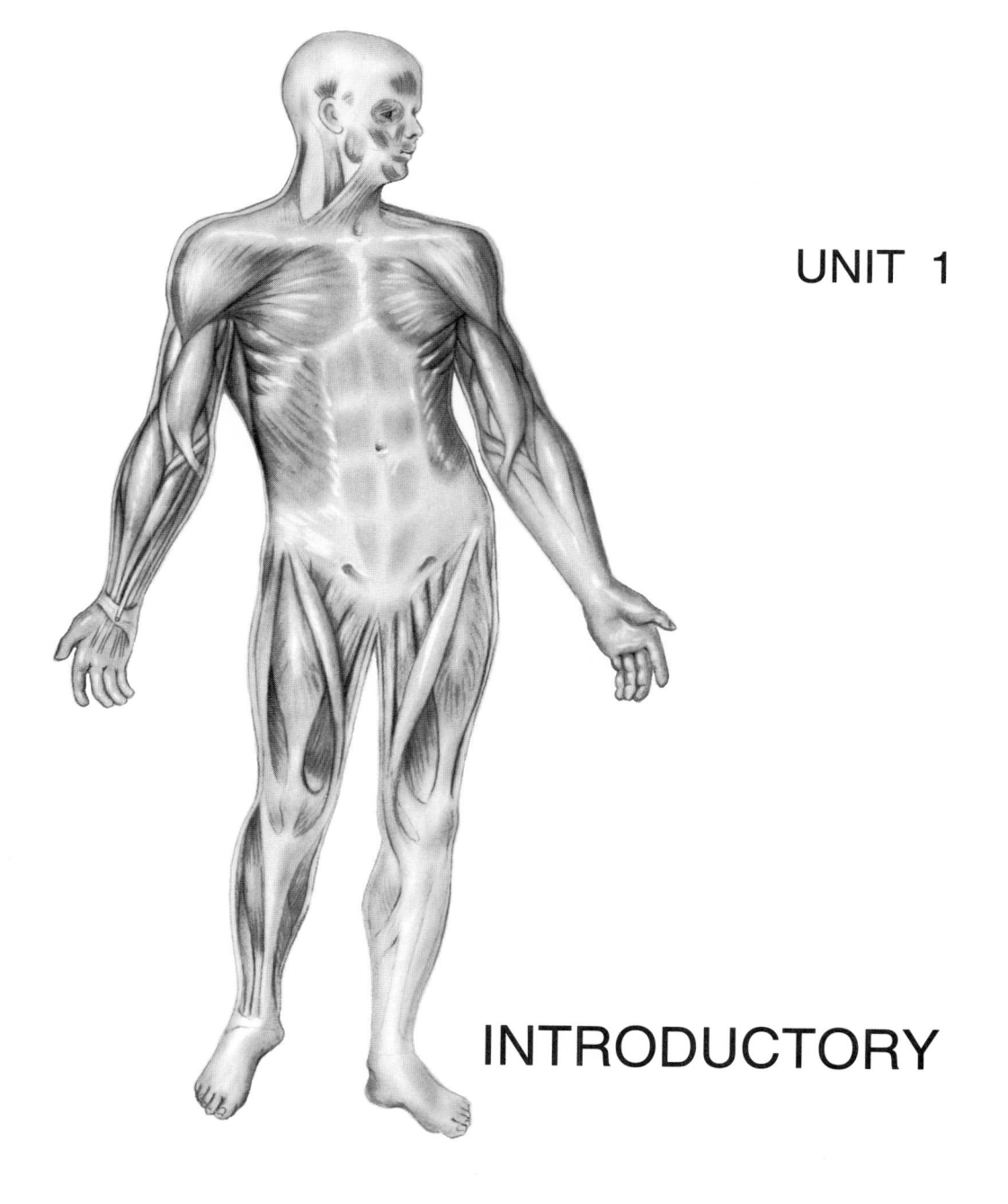

UNIT 1

INTRODUCTORY

Chapter 1

THE BODY AS A WHOLE

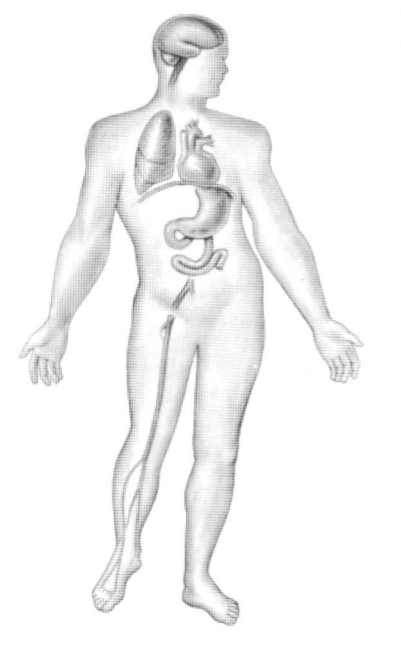

The human body is a complex machine and, like any machine, is an assembly of parts organized to function as a whole. To understand the body it is necessary to understand its components, their function, and their relationship to one another.

EXPERIMENT A: Planes of Organization of the body
EXPERIMENT B: Cavities and Organs of the Human Torso
EXPERIMENT C: Dissection of Small Laboratory Animal

EXPERIMENT A: Planes of Organization of the Body

References (see appendix for complete reference titles):
Jacob & Francone (hereinafter to be called J & F), Ch. 1; appropriate chapters in Anthony, Greisheimer, Dienhart, Chaffee & Greisheimer, and Kimber et al.

Objective: To understand the terminology employed in locating structures of the body.

Procedure:

1. Using the references indicated above familiarize yourself with the following terms:

Sagittal plane
Coronal plane
Transverse plane
Medial
Posterior (dorsal)

Anterior (ventral)
Cranial (superior)
Lateral aspect
Caudal (inferior)

2. Label Figure 1 with the above terms.

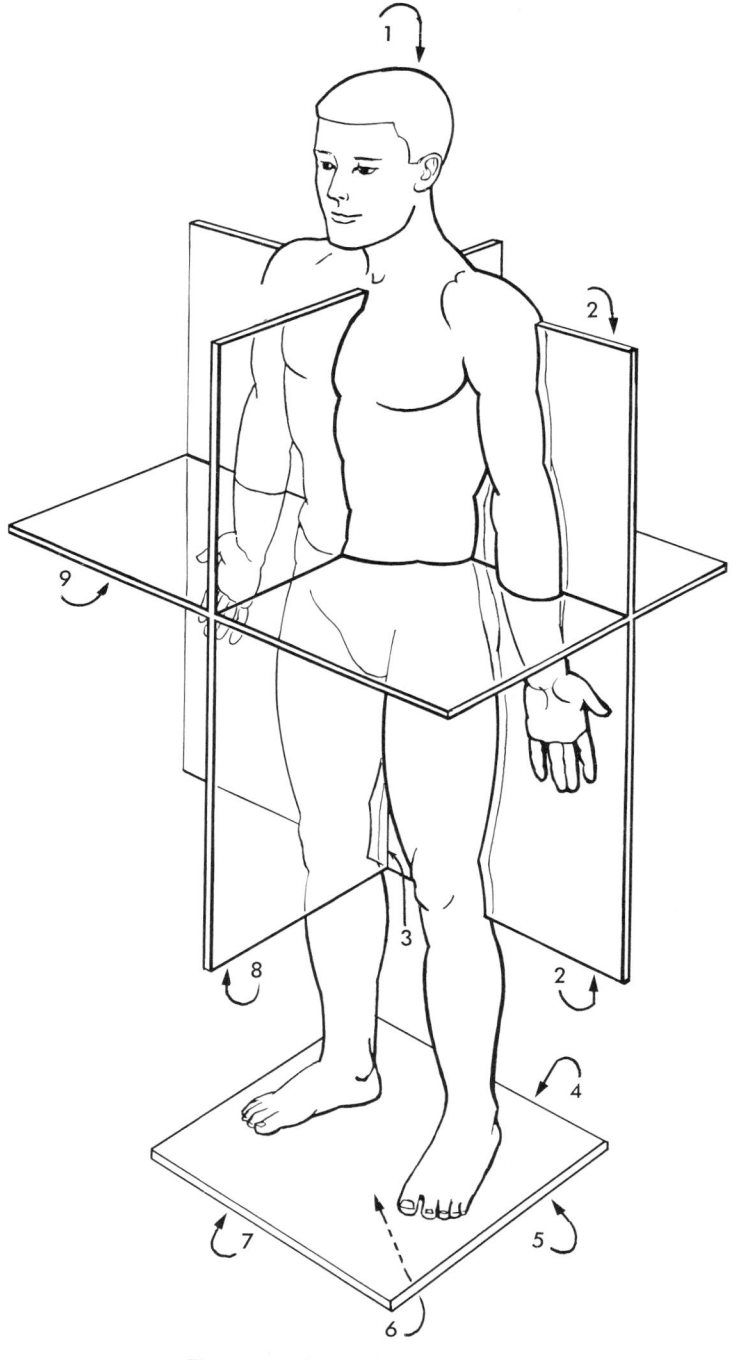

Figure 1. Planes of organization.

EXPERIMENT B: Cavities and Organs of the Human Torso

References:

J & F, Ch. 1; appropriate chapters in King & Showers, Kimber et al., Greisheimer, Chaffee & Greisheimer, Anthony.

Materials:

1. Model of human torso
2. Anatomic charts of human body

Objective: To develop a working knowledge of the positions of organs and systems within the body.

Procedure:

1. Using the references indicated above, remove and identify all the body organs in the model of the human torso, noting their size, position, shape, and the cavity (see below) in which each is located.

2. List the organs found in the following cavities:

CAVITY	ORGANS
Cranial	
Spinal	
Thoracic	
Abdominal	
Pelvic	

3. Label Figure 2 with the following terms:

Cranial cavity (dorsal)   Abdominal cavity (ventral)
Thoracic cavity (ventral) Pelvic cavity (ventral)
Spinal cavity (dorsal)   Respiratory diaphragm

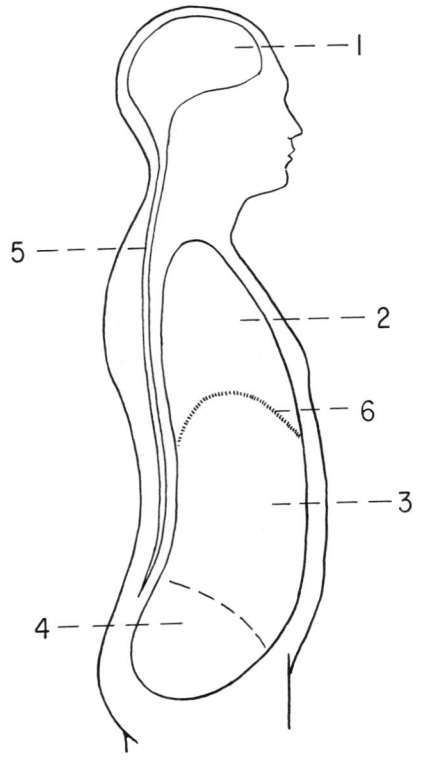

Figure 2. Cavities of the body.

EXPERIMENT C: Dissection of Laboratory Animal (instructors may wish to conserve animals by following Experiment C with Experiment A, Chapter 3)

References:

See appropriate animal dissection guide, page 255.

Materials:

1. Laboratory animal
2. Ether or, preferably, Nembutal
3. Dissecting instruments and trays:
   a. Large scissors (about 5½ in., one sharp-pointed blade, and one round-pointed blade)
   b. Small scissors (about 3 in.)
   c. Scalpel (one with replaceable blade if possible)
   d. Forceps (smooth and toothed)
   e. Probes (blunt, bent tip, and needle type)
   f. Pins
4. Normal saline solution (see appendix)
5. Gauze sponges

Objective: To become familiar with the relationships between the organs and systems in the living animal.

Procedure:

1. Anesthetize a laboratory animal by placing it and an ether-saturated gauze sponge in a glass jar with a tightly fitting lid. When the animal appears to be anesthetized, take the lid off the jar and pinch the animal with forceps. If it does not respond it is sufficiently anesthetized.

A *preferable* anesthetic to use for animal dissection is Veterinary Nembutal (60 mg. per ml.). Inject 1 ml. per 200 gm. of animal body weight intraperitoneally. A dose of around 2 ml. per 200 gm. will usually kill the animal. Since Nembutal may not be readily available, ether may be used.

If ether is used, keep an ether-saturated gauze sponge over the nose and mouth of the animal dissected *at all times* to avoid having the animal awaken during dissection.

2. After anesthetization, place animal ventral side up and pin to dissecting board. With a scalpel carefully make a midsagittal incision from pubis to sternum. When making the incision, be certain to cut only the skin. Next make lateral incisions on either side of pubis and sternum to lay the skin back and expose the abdominal muscles. Use a scalpel to free skin from underlying tissue. Keep animal moist with normal saline.

3. The abdominal cavity. Open the abdominal cavity by lifting the muscular attachment to the pubis and cutting from the pelvis to the sternum. Without disturbing the viscera, observe the position of the organs in the abdominal cavity (see Fig. 3). Using references indicated above, note the color and position of the following visceral organs:

   a. Liver: Note size, color, location, and relationship to the diaphragm.
   b. Gallbladder: (Note that the rat has no gallbladder.)
   c. Stomach: Note position, shape, size, and relationship to other organs and diaphragm.
   d. Small intestine: Gently lift the small intestine; note the mesentery and its method of attachment to the dorsal body wall. Follow along the length of the intestine and observe the vessels present in the mesentery. Note the junction of the small intestine and large intestine.

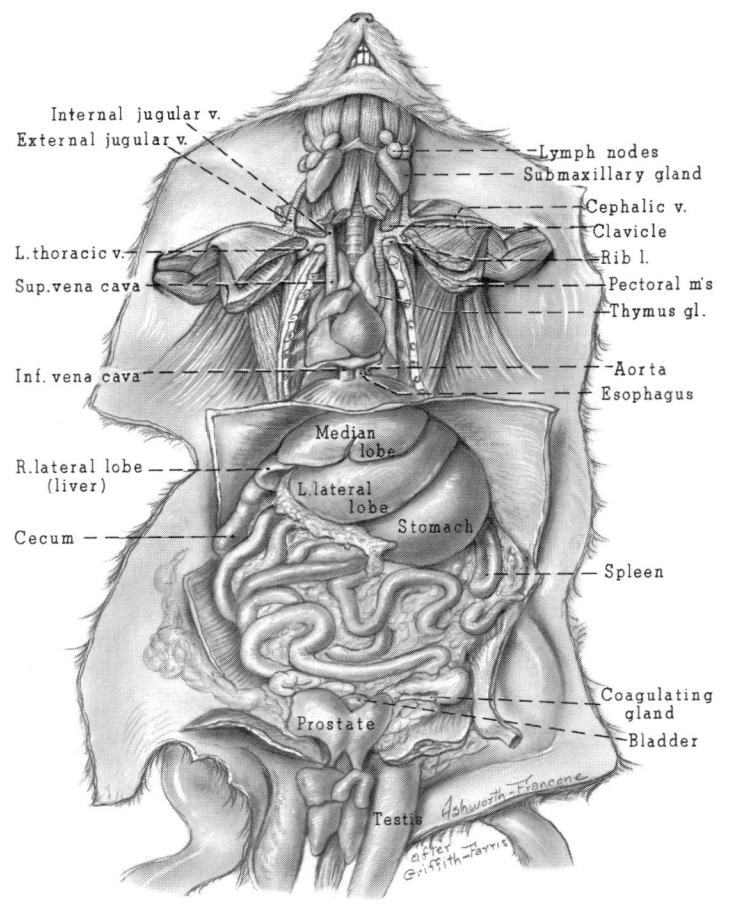

Internal jugular v.
External jugular v.
Lymph nodes
Submaxillary gland
Cephalic v.
Clavicle
L. thoracic v.
Sup. vena cava
Rib 1.
Pectoral m's
Thymus gl.
Inf. vena cava
Aorta
Esophagus
Median lobe
R. lateral lobe (liver)
L. lateral lobe
Stomach
Cecum
Spleen
Coagulating gland
Prostate
Bladder
Testis
after Griffith-Farris

Figure 3. Organs of thoracic and abdominal cavities.

   e. Large intestine: Lift the large intestine; note its size, position, and relationship to other organs. Observe the cecum and the ascending, transverse, and descending colon.
   f. Spleen: Identify this elongated, reddish brown organ situated below and to the left of the liver.
   g. Pancreas: Locate this small pinkish mass of tissue, irregular in shape, and located in the mesentery between the stomach and intestine.
   h. Kidneys: Locate the kidneys, one on either side of the vertebral column, fastened to the posterior body wall retroperitoneally. Note color and shape of kidneys, renal vessels, and ureters.
   i. Suprarenal glands: These are small pink bodies lying above each kidney.
4. The pelvic cavity:
   a. Ureters: Carefully lift the ureters with forceps and follow them to the bladder.
   b. Urinary bladder: Observe the shape, color, and relationship to other organs.

c. Urethra: Gently pull on the bladder and notice the location of the urethra. With scissors cut the tissues surrounding it so that relationship may be observed.

d. Reproductive organs (ovaries, testes): Observe position, size, and relationship.

5. The thoracic cavity:

a. Diaphragm: Gently pull the liver inferiorly and note the diaphragm. Observe the muscle and central tendon of the diaphragm. With scissors, continue the SKIN incision upward to the neck.

b. Pericardium: Pick up the body wall with forceps and cut through the thoracic wall in midline. Note that the pericardium is fastened to the diaphragm.

c. Heart: Lift the thoracic cage upward and outward; observe the location of the heart. Note atria, ventricles, and the great blood vessels entering and leaving the heart.

d. Lungs: These are pinkish, spongy organs that lie on either side of and partly behind the heart.

e. Pharynx: Cartilaginous and anterior to esophagus.

f. Esophagus: Posterior to pharynx. Leads to stomach.

6. The mouth. Note number and shape of teeth and tongue.

7. The extremities. Examine the fore and hind limbs. How many joints does each have? _____

8. When dissection is complete wrap the animal in paper towels or newspaper and dispose of it in an appropriate animal waste container.

Chapter 2

THE CELL

The cell is the basic structural and physiological unit of life. Each living cell possesses characteristics of growth, metabolism, irritability, and reproductive capacity.

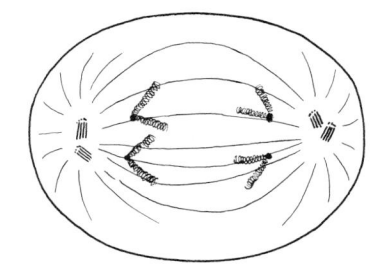

EXPERIMENT A: Examination of the microscope
EXPERIMENT B: Use of the Microscope

ANATOMY OF THE CELL

EXPERIMENT C: Typical Cell

PHYSIOLOGY OF THE CELL

EXPERIMENT D: Mitosis (Cell Division)
EXPERIMENT E: Chromosomes, DNA and RNA
(Optional)

EXPERIMENT A: Examination of the Microscope

References:
Allen, pp. 40-44; Needham, pp. 7-12; Gage, pp. 7-35.
Materials: Microscope
Objective: To gain a working knowledge of the microscope.
Procedure:

1. There are two lens systems in a compound microscope, whence its name. These systems complement each other, allowing greater resolution than is possible with a single system. A microscope consists of two major parts, the supporting stand and the optical system. There are several parts to each with which the student must be familiar before attempting to use it.

      a. Supporting stand:

Arm	Coarse adjustment
Stage	Fine adjustment
Stage clips or mechanical stage	Mirror
Condenser and iris diaphragm	Substage

      b. The optical system:

Eye
Drawtube
Objectives (usually three)

2. Label Figure 4 using the above terms.

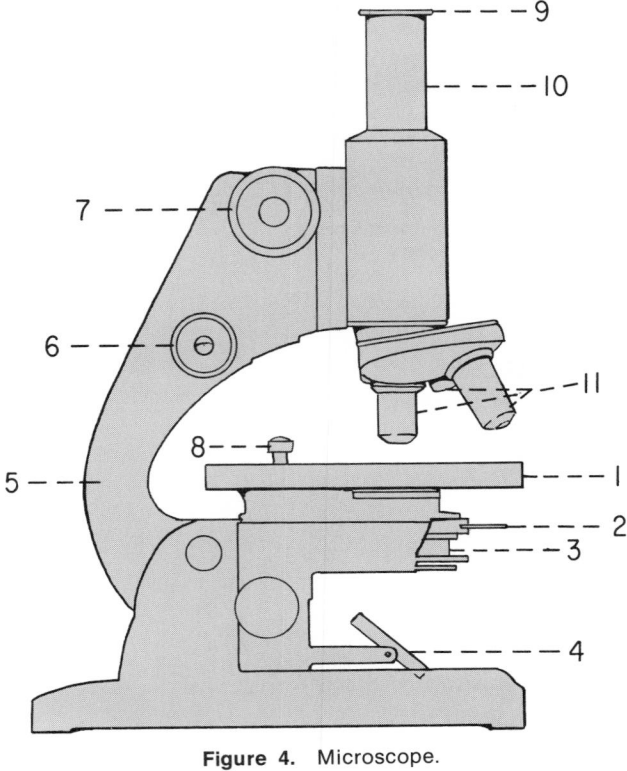

Figure 4. Microscope.

EXPERIMENT B: Use of the Microscope

Reference:
> Needham, pp. 381, 387.

Materials:
> 1. Microscope
> 2. Slides and cover slips
> 3. Toothpicks
> 4. Methylene blue stain (see appendix)
> 5. 95% alcohol

Objective: To provide experience in microscopic technique.

Procedure:

1. Take a toothpick and gently scrape the inside of your cheek. Deposit the material accumulated on the toothpick on a slide. Place a few drops of 95% alcohol on the slide. Next add one or two drops of methylene blue stain and cover with a cover slip.

2. Place the light source about 6 inches away from and at the same height as the stage. Direct light slightly downward to reduce glare. With the diaphragm open, adjust mirror to obtain maximum illumination. To be successful in the use of the microscope, it is critical that this technique be mastered.

3. Move the low power objective in position over the stage, about ¾ of an inch away.

4. Position the slide on the stage with the material to be observed over the opening.

5. Carefully bring the material into focus with the coarse adjustment. Next, using the diaphragm only, adjust the light for maximum clarity.

6. Position the high power objective and finish focusing with *fine adjustment*. (Do not use coarse adjustment or you may break the slide.) Microscopes are made so that after one objective is in focus the others should also be in focus with only a minor change of the fine adjustment.

7. Always use lens paper to clean the eyepiece and the objectives. Never touch with fingers. Fingers leave an oil-like deposit on the objectives, and materials other than lens paper may scratch the lenses. When returning microscope to storage, always have the low power objective in position over the stage.

8. Save slide for Experiment C.

ANATOMY OF THE CELL

EXPERIMENT C: The Typical Cell

References:

    J & F; Appropriate chapters in Anthony, Kimber et al., Chaffee, Dienhart, Guyton, Reith et al.

Materials:

    1. Slide from previous experiment

    2. Microscope

Objective: To observe cell structure.

Procedure:

    1. Using the references indicated above, examine slide under high power. Identify the following:

Cell membrane	Nucleolus
Vacuoles	Nucleus
Nuclear membrane	

    2. Study Figure 5.

    3. Is there really such a thing as "a typical cell"? Support your answer.

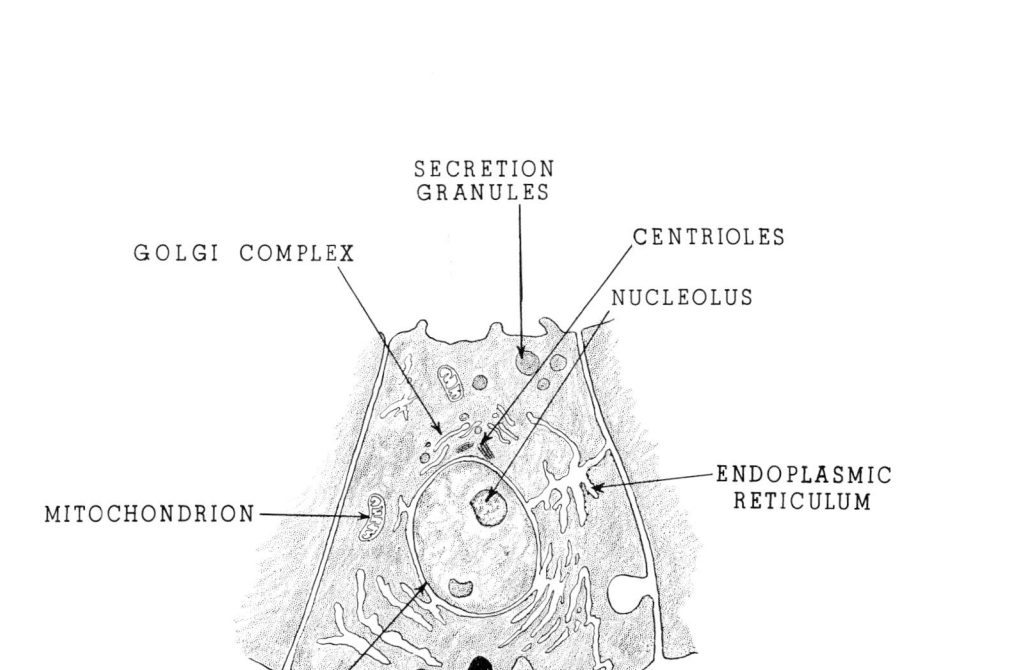

Figure 5. The cell.

PHYSIOLOGY OF THE CELL

EXPERIMENT D: Mitosis (Cell Division)

References:
> J & F, Ch. 2; appropriate chapters in Guyton, Decoursey, King & Showers, Chaffee & Greisheimer, Greisheimer, Kimber et al., Anthony, Swanson.

Materials:
> 1. Microscope
> 2. Histologic sections of whitefish embryo (blastoderm stage) showing mitosis.

Objective: To observe mitosis in animal cells.

Procedure:
> 1. Using the references indicated above, examine the slides provided and find all the phases of mitosis listed below. You will note that there are several sections on each slide. Examine all, since some will show certain phases more clearly than others.

Interphase	Anaphase
Prophase	Telophase
Metaphase	Daughter cells

> 2. Label Figure 6 with the above terms and those listed below.

Nucleus	Equatorial plate
Centrosome	Spindle fibers
Chromosomes	

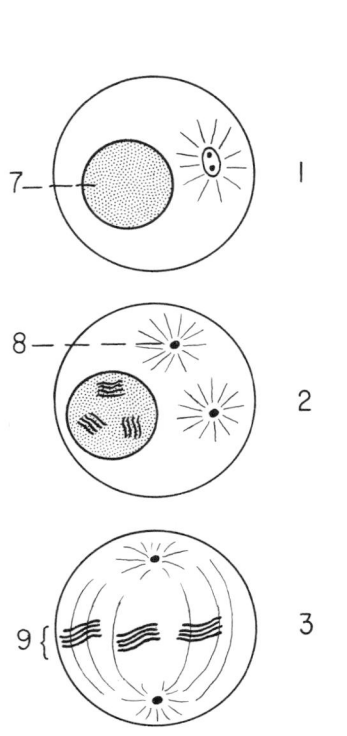

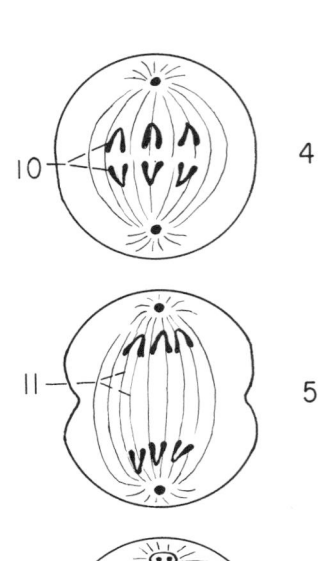

Figure 6. Mitosis.

EXPERIMENT E: Chromosomes, DNA and RNA (optional)

References:

J & F, Ch. 2; appropriate chapters in Anthony, Kimber et al., King & Showers, Guyton.

Materials:

Plastic models of DNA and RNA molecule

Objective: To understand how DNA and RNA reproduce and control cell activity.

Procedure:

1. Using the references indicated above examine models and Figure 7 and identify the following:

Adenine	Uracil
Quanine	Phosphate
Cytosine	Deoxyribose sugar
Thymine	A nucleotide
Ribose sugar	

2. Using the references indicated above discuss the meaning of the following terms:

Genetic code	Chromosome
DNA	Ribosome
RNA	Messenger RNA

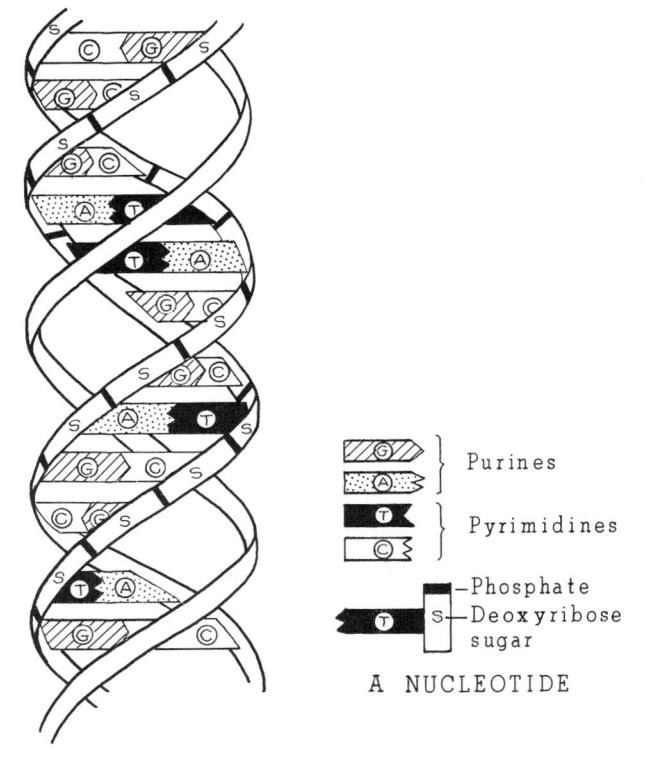

Figure 7. DNA.

PRACTICAL EXERCISE

1. Which part of the cell is most necessary for cell division? _____

2. Define mitosis: _____

3. List the four dividing stages of mitosis: _____

Chapter 3

TISSUES

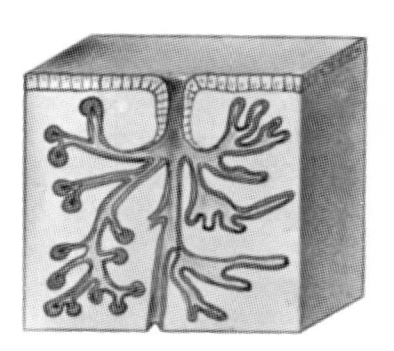

Each organ of the body is composed of tissues. A tissue is an organized group of specialized cells performing a specific function. There are four major types, each subdivided many times. The student should learn to distinguish these tissues in structure and function.

ANATOMY OF TISSUES
EXPERIMENT A: Gross Anatomy of Tissues
EXPERIMENT B: Histology of Tissues

ANATOMY OF TISSUES

EXPERIMENT A: Gross Anatomy of Tissues

References:
> See appropriate animal dissection guide.

Materials:
1. Laboratory animal
2. Dissecting instruments and tray
3. Gauze sponges
4. Normal saline (see appendix)
5. Ether or Nembutal

Objective: To observe the gross characteristics of tissues found in the body.

Procedure:

1. Anesthetize a laboratory animal (follow procedure in Chapter 1, Experiment C). Pin to dissecting board with ventral side up and make incision from the pubis to the jaw. Open the abdomen, chest, and neck, being careful not to damage the internal structures. Keep animal moist with normal saline.

2. Examine the internal organs for the following tissues:

TISSUE	LOCATION
Epithelial tissue	
Simple squamous	Body cavities (mesothelium), cardiovascular and lymphatic vessels (endothelium), terminal respiratory ducts, alveoli
Simple cuboidal	Many glands; pigmented epithelium of the retina
Simple columnar	Digestive tract from the lower esophagus to the anus, uterus, uterine tubes, bronchioles, gallbladder
Pseudostratified columnar	Nasal cavity, trachea, bronchi
Stratified squamous	Epidermis (skin), mouth and tongue, esophagus, anus, vagina, cornea, conjunctiva *(continued)*

TISSUE	LOCATION
Stratified cuboidal	Tubules of testis, graafian follicles of ovary, ducts of sweat glands, sebaceous glands
Stratified columnar	Pharynx and larynx
Transitional epithelium	Urinary tract
Connective tissue proper	
Loose connective tissue	
Areolar	Loosely arranged fibroelastic tissue between organs and muscles; supports blood vessels and nerves
Adipose	Subcutaneous fat, breast, bone marrow
Reticular	Framework of liver, lymphoid tissues, marrow, gastrointestinal tract, respiratory mucous membranes
Dense connective tissue	
Regular	Tendons, aponeuroses, ligaments
Irregular	Fasciae, capsules, sheaths, septa
Specialized connective tissue	
Cartilage	
Hyaline	Articular surfaces of bones, costal cartilages, trachea, tip of nose, larynx, fetal skeleton
Fibrous	Discs between vertebrae; symphysis pubis; knee and hip joints
Elastic	Auricle of external ear, auditory tube, epiglottis, cartilages of larynx
Bone	Skeleton
Dentin	Teeth
Hematopoietic (marrow) and bone	Marrow spaces of bones and vascular system
Lymphoid	Lymph nodes, thymus, spleen, tonsils, adenoids
Muscular tissue	
Striated skeletal (voluntary)	Skeletal muscles; muscles of the tongue, pharynx, larynx; extrinsic muscles of the eye
Smooth (involuntary)	Muscular walls of the digestive and urinary tracts, blood vessels
Cardiac	Heart
Nervous tissue	
Nervous tissue proper	Neurons and nerve fibers
Neuroglia	Supportive tissue in central nervous system

EXPERIMENT B: Histology of Tissues

References:

   J & F, Ch. 3; Hamm & Leeson, latest edition. Use index to find appropriate tissue in Guyton, Reith, Kimber et al. Any good histology book will illustrate cell structure by means of photomicrographs.

Materials:

   1. Histologic sections of tissues studied in Experiment A (bone, muscle, and nervous tissue will be studied in detail in their respective chapters)

   2. Microscope

Objective: To observe microscopic characteristics of tissues.

Procedure:

   1. Using the references indicated above, examine sections of the various tissues; note the differences in:

   a. size and shape of cells

   b. presence of intercellular materials

   c. presence of cell organelles

   2. Fill in the following chart as you examine the various tissues.

TISSUE	SCHEMATIC TISSUE DRAWING
A. *Epithelial tissue*	
Simple squamous	
Simple cuboidal	
Simple columnar	
Pseudostratified columnar	
Stratified squamous	
Stratified cuboidal	
Stratified columnar	
Transitional epithelium	
B. *Connective tissue proper*	
Loose connective tissue	
Areolar	

(Continued)

TISSUE	SCHEMATIC TISSUE DRAWING

Adipose

Reticular

Dense connective tissue

Regular

Irregular

Specialized connective tissue

Cartilage

Hyaline

Fibrous

Elastic

Bone

Dentin

Hematopoietic (marrow)
and bone

Lymphoid

C. *Muscular tissue*

Striated skeletal
(voluntary)

Smooth (involuntary)

Cardiac

D. *Nervous tissue*

(Continued)

TISSUE	SCHEMATIC TISSUE DRAWING
Nervous tissue proper	
Neuroglia	

PRACTICAL EXERCISE

1. Distinguish the three types of muscle tissue: _____

_____

2. Why is transplanted tissue usually rejected?_____

_____

UNIT 2

FRAMEWORK
OF THE BODY

Chapter 4

SKIN

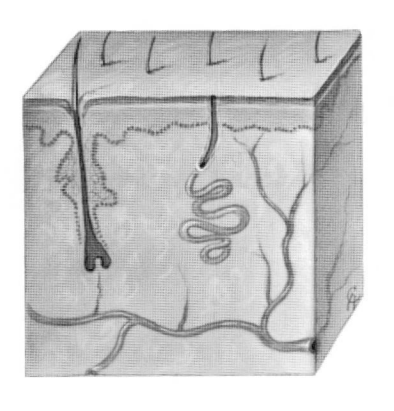

The integument or outer covering of the body is normally referred to as the skin. It covers and protects the tissue lying beneath it and is abundantly supplied with sensory nerve endings which are influenced by environmental stimuli. The derivatives of skin exhibit variation in different regions of the body.

ANATOMY OF THE SKIN
EXPERIMENT: Histology of the Skin

ANATOMY OF THE SKIN

EXPERIMENT: Histology of the Skin

References:
> J & F, Ch. 4; appropriate chapters in Chaffee & Greisheimer, King & Showers, Decoursey, Reith et al., Anthony, Kimber et al.

Materials:
> Histologic sections of skin (thick skin—sole of foot; thin skin)

Objective: To observe microscopic characteristics of skin.

Procedure:

1. Using the references indicated above, examine histologic sections of skin and find the following structures:

Stratum corneum	Epidermis
Stratum lucidum	Dermis
Stratum germinativum	Dense connective tissue
(malpighian layer)	Sweat Gland Secretory unit
Subcutaneous tissue	Sweat duct
Adipose tissue	Arteries
Muscle	Veins

2. Label Figure 8 using the above terms.

3. Place a short strand of hair on a slide. Cover with a cover slip. Examine under low and high power, and identify hair root, hair shaft, medulla, cortex, and cuticle.

4. Examine your fingernails and identify the lateral nail groove, nail fold, and lunula.

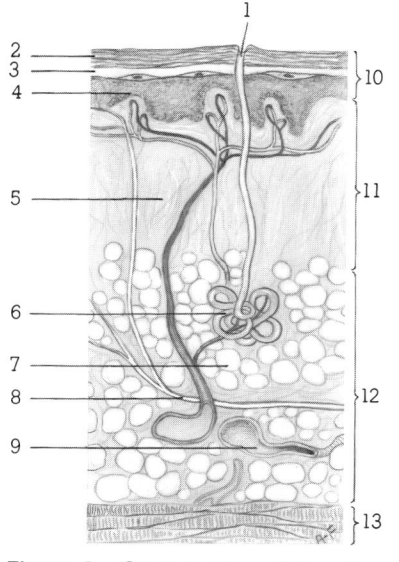

Figure 8. Cross section of the skin.

PRACTICAL EXERCISES

ANATOMY AND PHYSIOLOGY QUESTIONS:

    1. Discuss the function of sebaceous glands: _____

_____

_____

_____

_____

    2. Define melanin; melanocytes: _____

_____

_____

_____

_____

    3. List from superficial to deep the five layers of the epidermis: _____

_____

_____

_____

_____

    4. What causes hair to stand up when one is cold? _____

_____

_____

_____

_____

    5. How do blood vessels in the skin help regulate body temperature? ____

_____

_____

_____

_____

CLINICAL QUESTIONS:

    1. Why does a hypodermic injection hurt at some times but not at others?

_____

_____

_____

_____

2. Define the following terms:

Dermatitis _____

_____

_____

Diaphoresis _____

_____

_____

Chapter 5

THE SKELETAL SYSTEM

The skeletal system is the basic system of protection and movement in the body. It protects the brain and other vital parts from injury, provides the levers on which the muscles act during body movement, forms the chamber making respiration possible and takes part in production of blood cells.

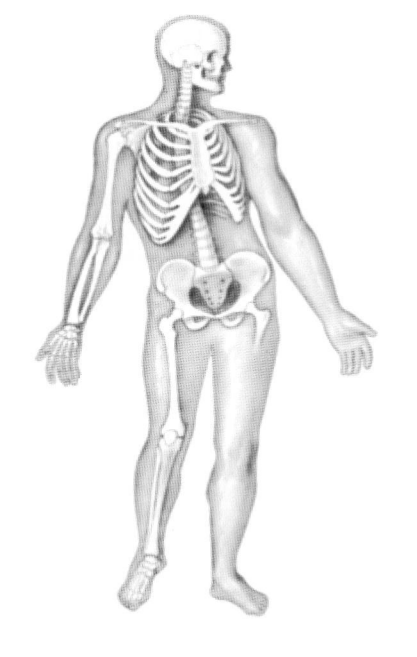

ANATOMY OF THE SKELETAL SYSTEM
EXPERIMENT A: Articulated Skeleton and Individual Bones
EXPERIMENT B: Fetal Skull
EXPERIMENT C: Histology of Bone

PHYSIOLOGY OF THE SKELETAL SYSTEM
EXPERIMENT D: Chemical Composition of Bone
PRACTICAL EXERCISES

ANATOMY OF THE SKELETAL SYSTEM

EXPERIMENT A: Articulated Skeleton and Individual Bones

References:
J & F, Ch. 5; appropriate chapters in Greisheimer, Kimber et al., Anthony, Reith et al., King & Showers, Dienhart, Chaffee & Greisheimer (good x-rays).

Materials:
1. Articulated and disarticulated skeleton
2. X-ray films (if available)

Objective: To examine individual bones relating physical characteristics to function.

Procedure:
1. Using the references indicated above, examine the parts of the articulated and disarticulated skeleton listed on the following pages.
2. Examine the x-ray films and identify as many structures as possible.
3. After examining the bones and structures in each group label Figures 9 to 23.

      a. Skull (front and side views, Figs. 9 and 10)

Frontal bone	Mandible
Lesser wing of sphenoid	Maxilla
Greater wing of sphenoid	Vomer
Ethmoid	Nares
Zygomatic bone	Lacrimal bone
Perpendicular plate of	Temporal bone
ethmoid	Parietal bone

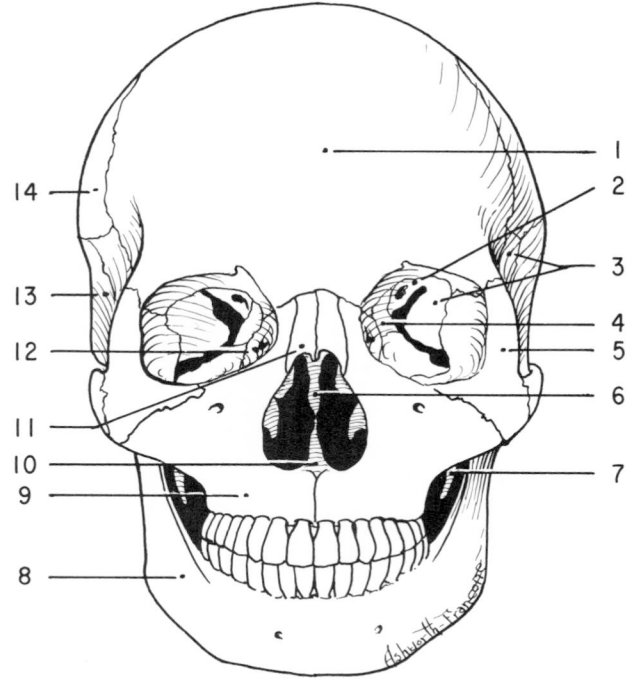

Figure 9. Frontal view of the skull.

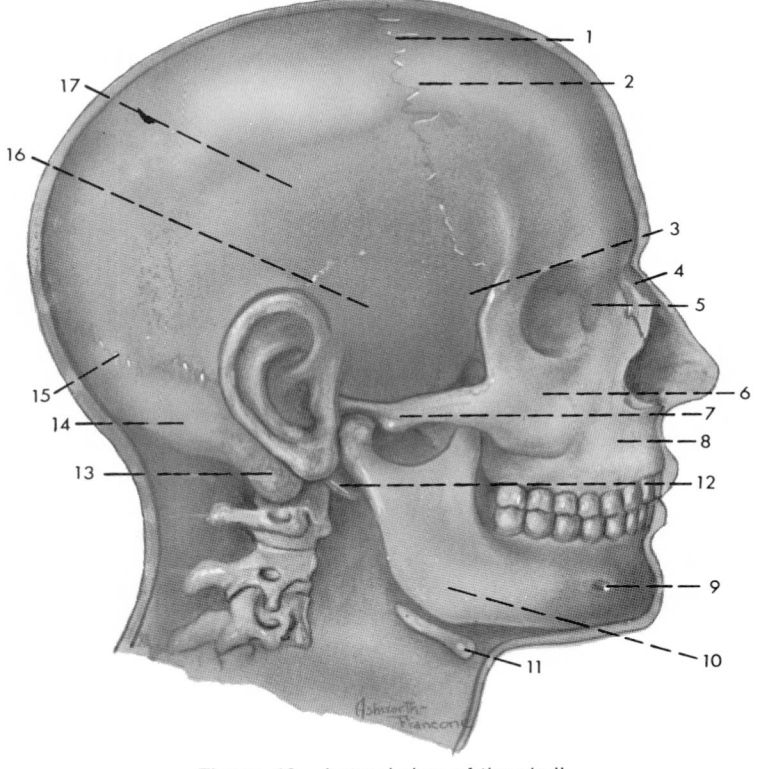

Figure 10. Lateral view of the skull.

Styloid process of temporal
Hyoid Bone
Mastoid process of temporal
Occipital bone
b. Inferior surface of skull (Fig. 11)
Palatine process of
   maxilla
Maxilla
Zygomatic bone
Greater wing of sphenoid
Zygomatic arch of temporal

Lambdoid suture
Mental foramen
Zygomatic arch of temporal
Coronal suture

Pterygoid process of
   sphenoid
Temporal bone
Foramen magnum
Medial pterygoid fossa of
   sphenoid

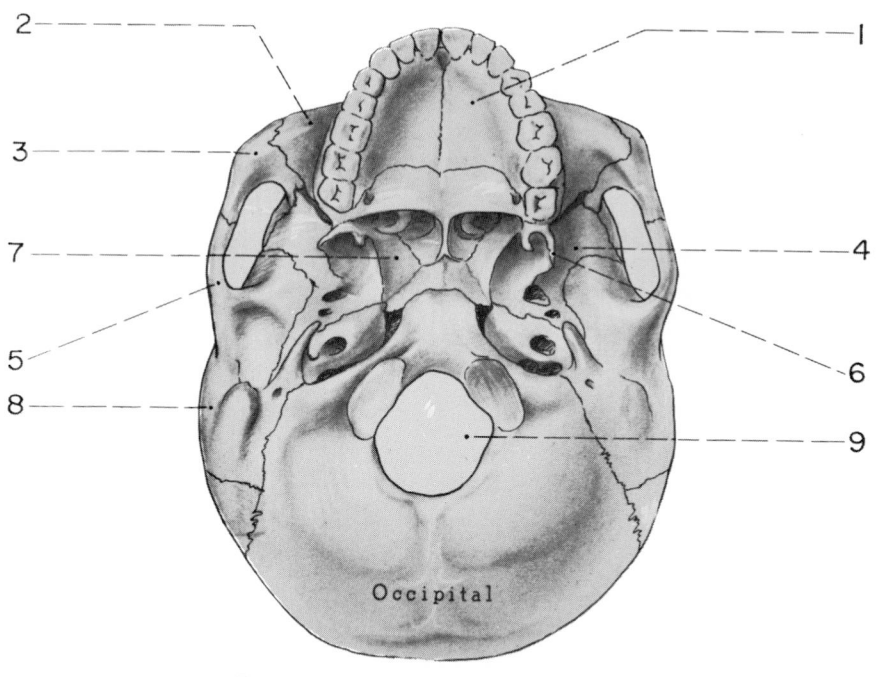

Occipital

Figure 11. Inferior surface of the skull.

c. Vertebral column (Fig. 12)

Occipital bone
Atlas (vertebra)
Axis (vertebra)
Transverse process
Rib
Coccyx
Superior articular process
Mandible
Lamina
Spinous process
Sacral canal
Sacral hiatus
Sacral foramen

Superior articular surface
Medial sacral crest
Promontory
Inferior articular process
Posterior transverse process
Vertebral foramen
Sacrum
Vertebral body
Transverse foramen
Articular facets for head of ribs
Inferior articular facets
Pedicle

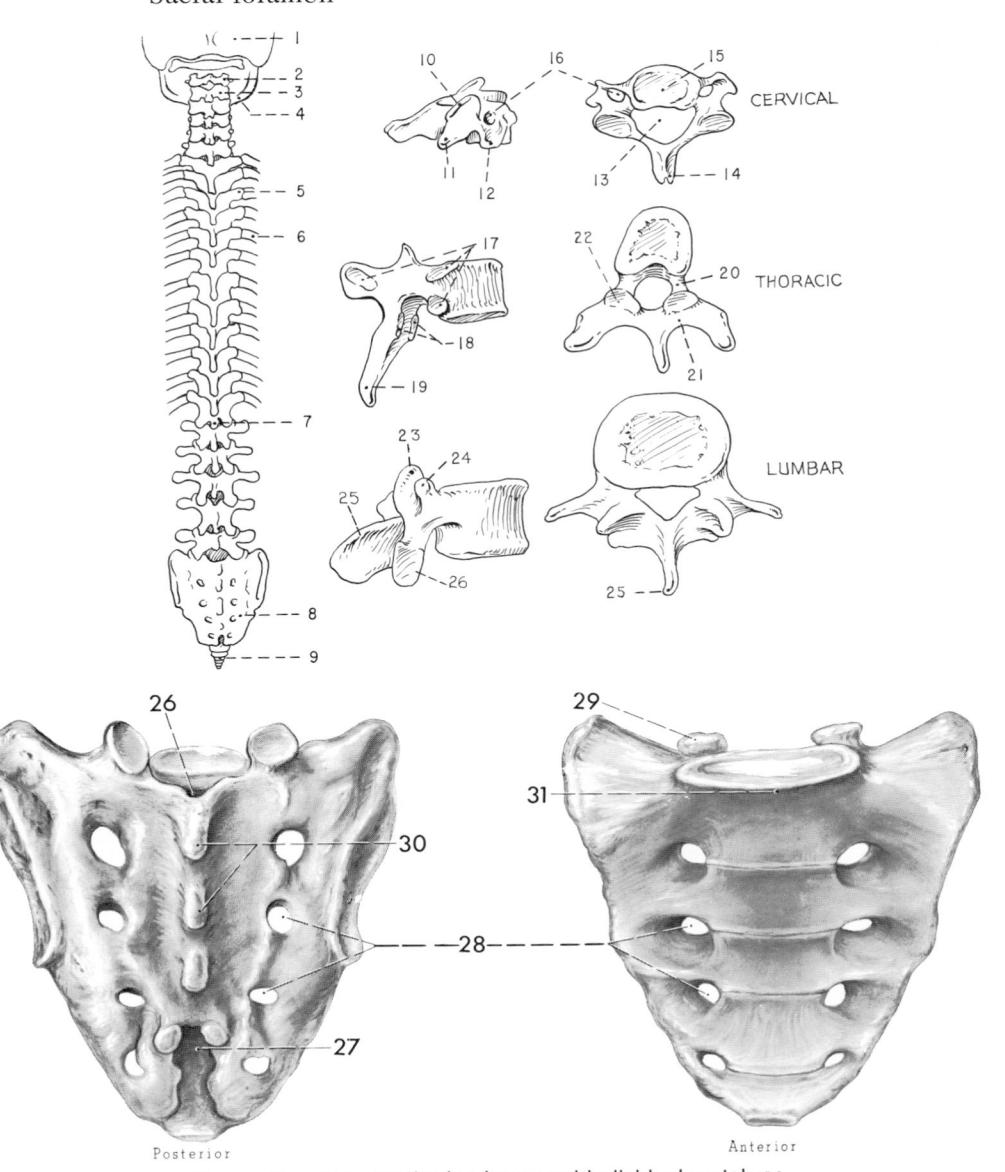

Figure 12. The vertebral column and individual vertebrae.

d. Scapula (Fig. 13)
  Supraspinous fossa
  Acromion
  Coracoid process
  Glenoid cavity
  Spine
  Infraglenoid tubercle

  Infraspinous fossa
  Medial border (vertebral)
  Lateral border (axillary)
  Inferior border
  Superior border

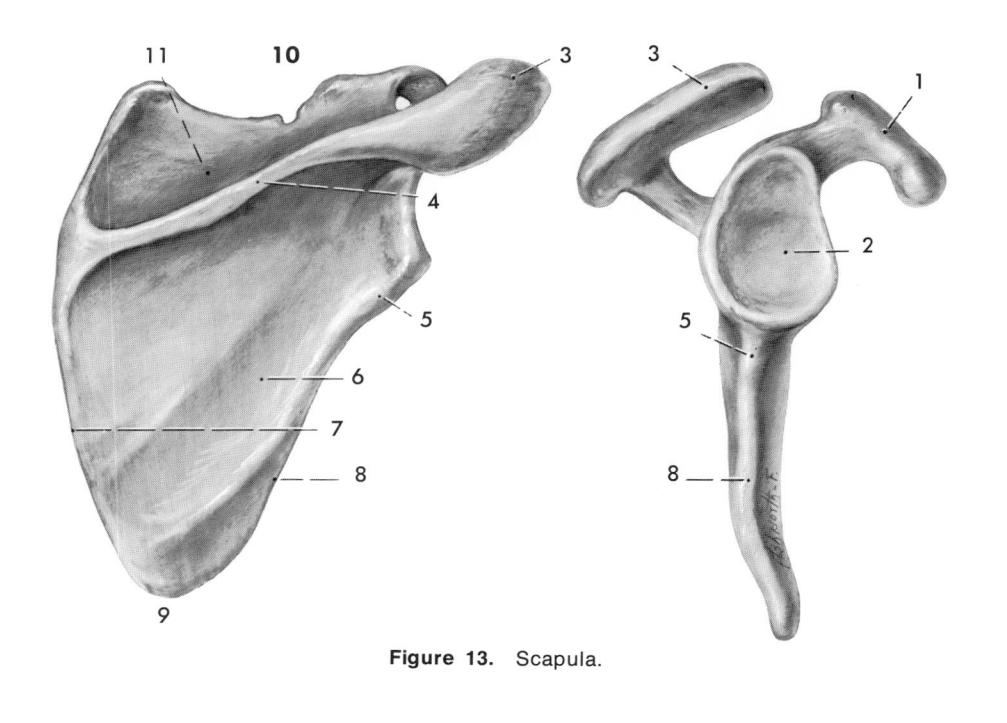

Figure 13. Scapula.

e. Thorax (Figs. 14 and 15)

Sternoclavicular joint	Sternochondral joint
Clavicle	Intercostal space
Acromioclavicular joint	Costal margin
Acromal process	Xiphoid process
Costochondral joint	Glenoid cavity
Costal cartilage	Coracoid process
Costotransverse joint	Transverse process
Suprasternal notch	Lamina of vertebrae
Manubrium of sternum	Scapula
Body of sternum	

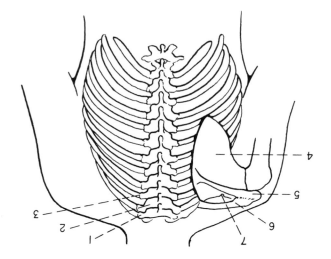

Figure 15. Posterior view of the thorax.

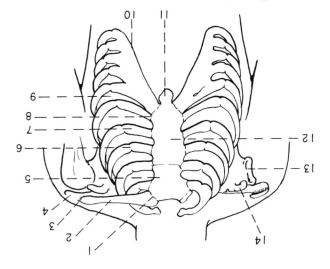

Figure 14. Anterior view of the thorax.

f. Rib (Fig. 16)

Tubercle   Neck

Head   Angle

Shaft   Costal extremity

Subcostal groove

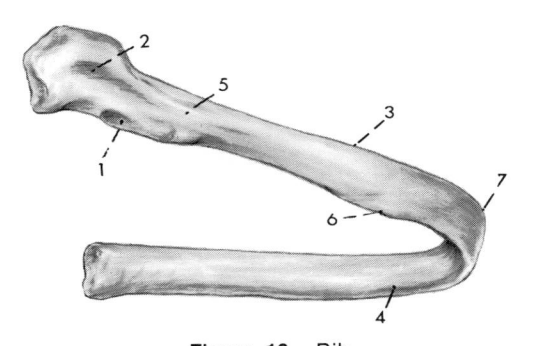

Figure 16. Rib.

g. Right upper extremity (Fig. 17)

Clavicle
Capitulum of humerus
Trochlea of humerus
Neck of humerus
Lesser tubercle of humerus
Head of humerus
Acromioclavicular joint
Sternoclavicular joint
Medial epicondyle of
  humerus
Shaft of humerus
Bicipital groove of humerus

Acromial process of clavicle
Coracoid process of scapula
Manubrium of sternum
Body of sternum
Costal cartilage
Rib
Superior radioulnar joint
Head of radius
Ulna
Scapula
First rib
Greater tubercle of humerus

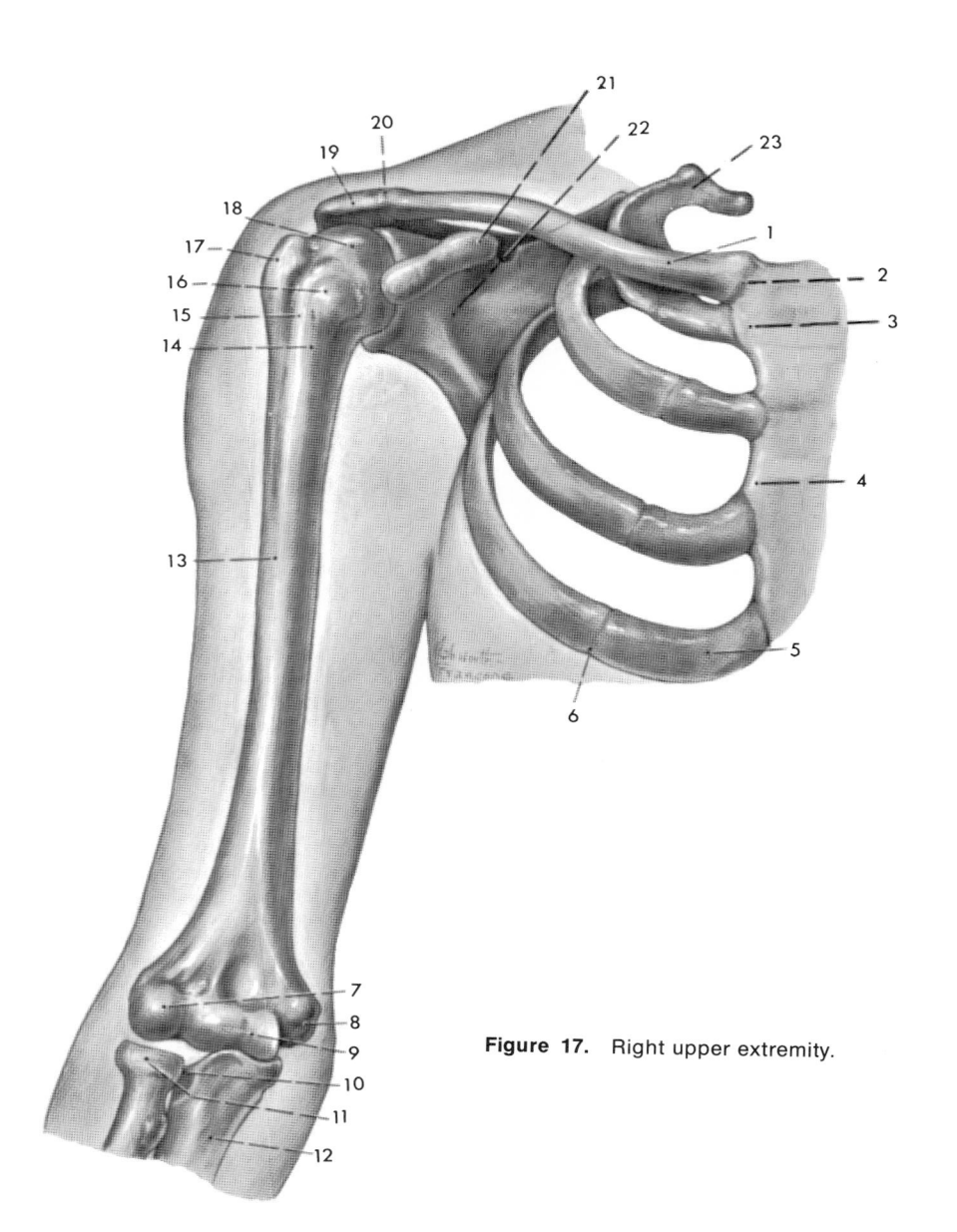

Figure 17. Right upper extremity.

h. Right forearm and hand (Fig. 18)

Trochlea of humerus
Ulna
Lunate
Hamate
Hook of hamate
Metacarpals
Trapezium
Scaphoid
Bicipital tuberosity of
    radius
Head of radius

Superior radioulnar joint
Inferior radioulnar joint
Triquetrum
Pisiform
Phalanges
Trapezoid
Capitate
Radius
Neck of radius
Capitulum
Humerus

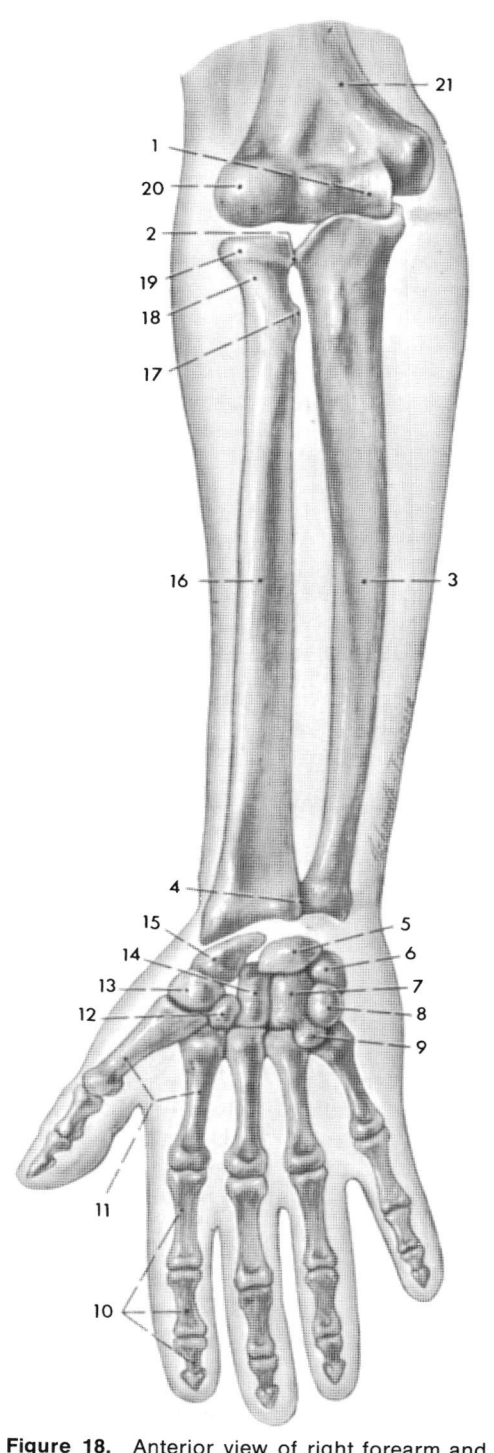

Figure 18. Anterior view of right forearm and hand.

i. Pelvic bone (Figs. 19 and 20). Note difference between male
   and female.

Iliac crest	Ischium
Posterior inferior spine	Anterior inferior spine
Greater sciatic notch	Acetabular fossa
Spine of ischium	Acetabular notch
Lesser sciatic notch	Superior ramus of pubis
Obturator foramen	Pubic crest
Inferior ramus of ischium	Inferior ramus of pubis
Sacroiliac joint	Symphysis pubis
Anterior superior spine	Posterior superior spine
Anterior superior iliac spine	Iliac fossa
Ilium	Greater trochanter
Pubis	Vertebra

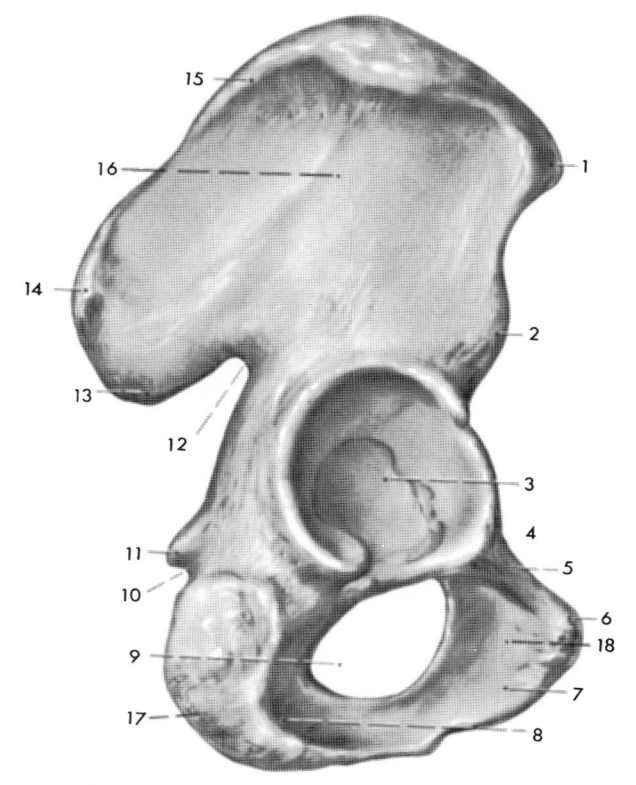

Figure 19. Lateral view of right pelvic bone.

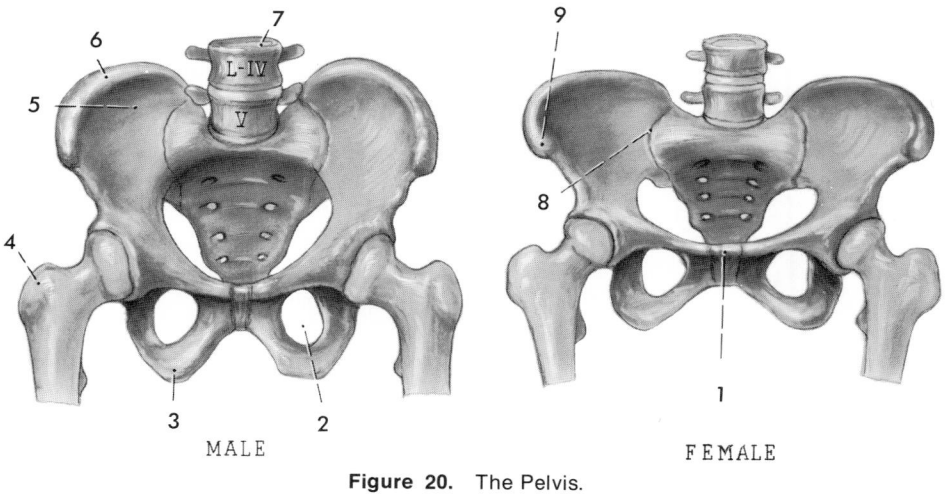

MALE

FEMALE

Figure 20. The Pelvis.

j. Bones of leg (Fig. 21)

Greater trochanter of femur
Lesser trochanter of femur
Shaft of femur
Adductor tubercle of femur
Lateral femoral condyle of
    femur
Patella
Fibula
Shaft of tibia
Medial malleolus of tibia
Head of fibula
Neck of femur
Head of femur
Medial femoral condyle
Lateral malleolus of tibia
Sacroiliac joint
Lumbosacral joint
Pubic symphysis
Phalanges

Anterior superior iliac spine
    of pelvic bone
Anterior inferior iliac spine
    of pelvic bone
Tarsus
Calcaneum
Metatarsus
Talus
Ischial spine of pelvic bone
Posterior inferior iliac spine
    of pelvic bone
Spinous process of sacrum
Sacrum
Posterior superior iliac spine
    of pelvic bone
Coccyx
Obturator foramen
Ischial tuberosity of
    pelvic bone

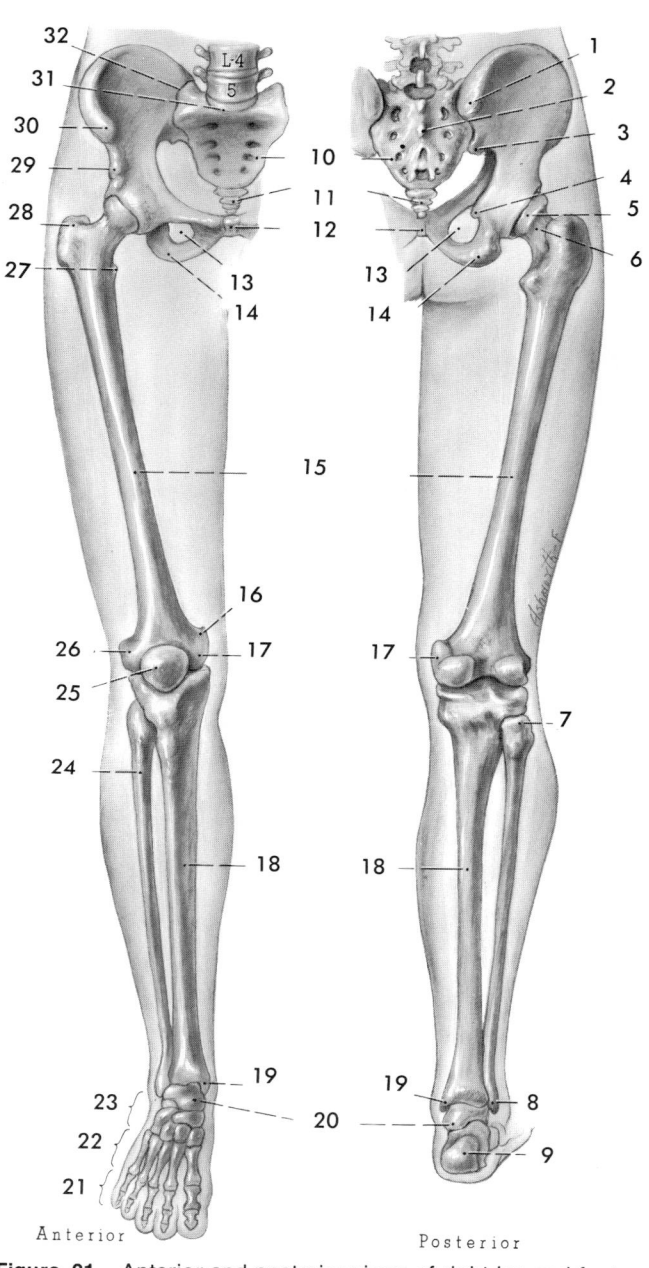

Figure 21. Anterior and posterior views of right leg and foot.

k. Bones of Foot (Fig. 22)
    Navicular (scaphoid)   Calcaneus
    Talus (astragalus)   Distal phalanges
    First, second, third   Middle phalanges
        cuneiform   Proximal phalanges
    Metatarsals   Cuboid

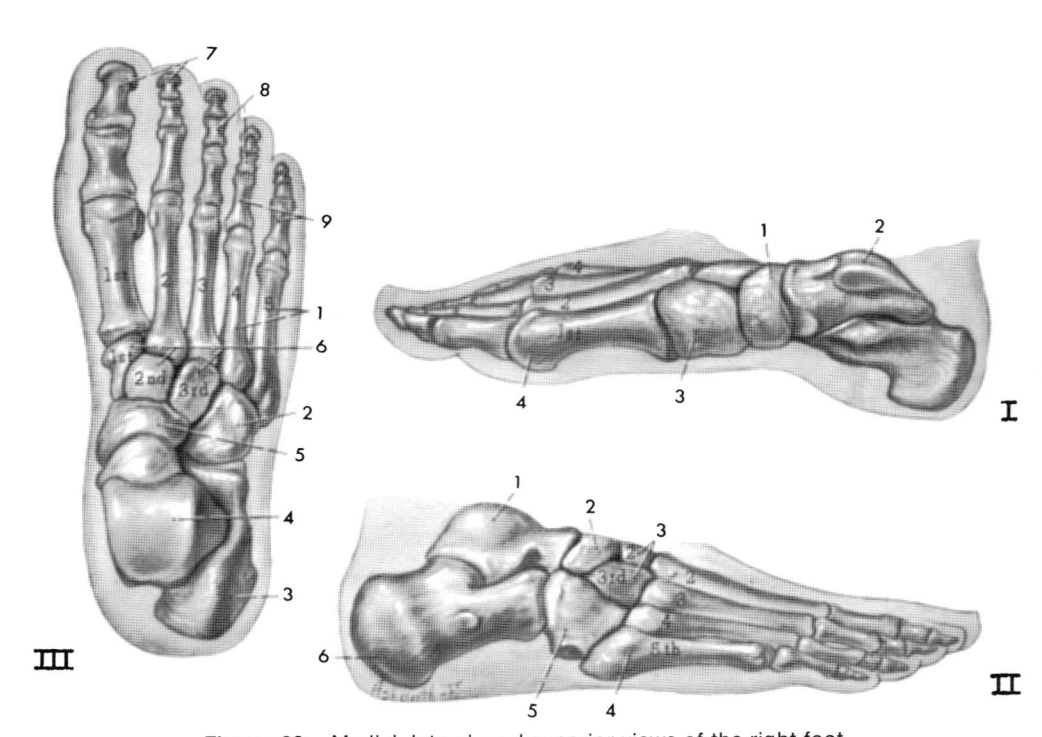

Figure 22. Medial, lateral, and superior views of the right foot.

EXPERIMENT B: Fetal Skull

References:
> J & F, Ch. 5; appropriate chapters in Greisheimer, Kimber et al., Reith
> et al., Dienhart, Chaffee & Greisheimer.

Materials: Fetal skull showing fontanels

Procedure:
> 1. Examine fetal skulls and note the following structures:

Anterior lateral fontanel	Lambdoidal suture
Occipital bone	Posterior lateral fontanel
Frontal fontanel	Squamous suture
Occipital fontanel	Coronal suture

> 2. Label Fig. 23 with the above terms.

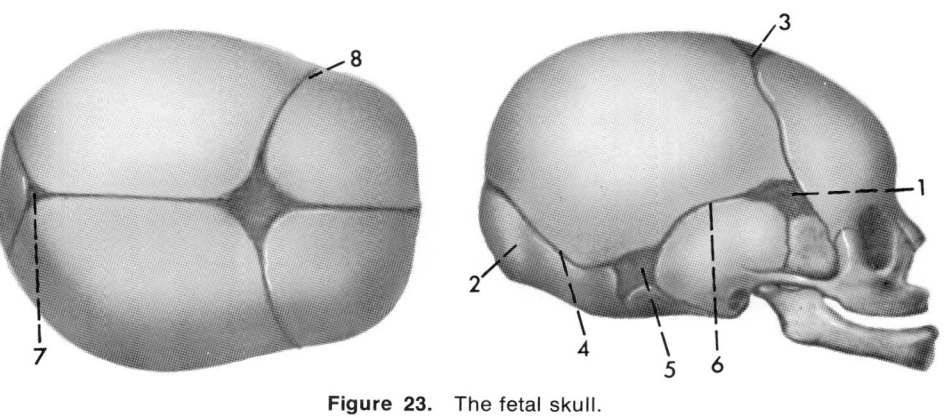

Figure 23.   The fetal skull.

EXPERIMENT C: Histology of Bone

References:
> J & F, Ch. 5; appropriate chapters in Greisheimer, Kimber et al., Reith et al., King & Showers, Chaffee & Greisheimer, Ham & Leeson. Any good histology book will illustrate cell structure by means of photomicrographs.

Materials:
> 1. Beef or other bone sawed in half longitudinally and medially
> 2. Histologic sections of bone tissue

Objective: To understand the relationship of the internal structure of bone to its functions.

Procedure:
> 1. Using the references indicated above, examine the beef bones and slides and note the following structures:

Articular cartilage	Haversian canal
Spongy bone (cancellous)	Concentric lamellae
Compact bone	Osteocytes
Lacunae	Periosteum
Canaliculi	Volkmann's canal

> 2. Label Figure 24 with the above terms.

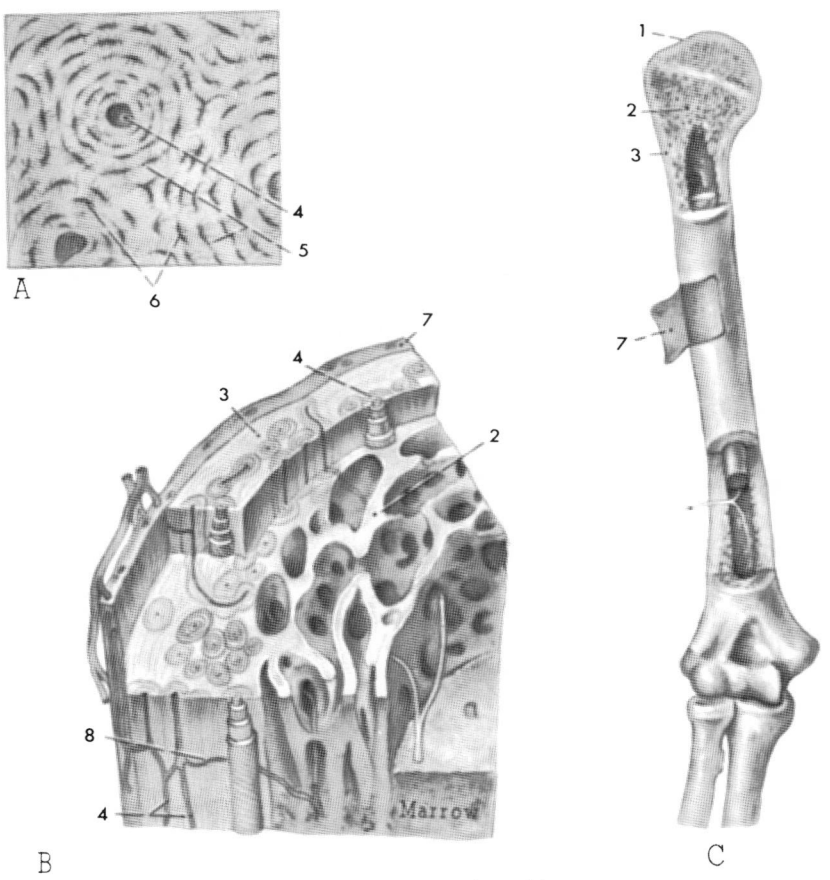

Figure 24. Cross section of bone.

PHYSIOLOGY OF THE SKELETAL SYSTEM

EXPERIMENT D: Chemical Composition of Bone

References:

J & F, Ch. 5; appropriate chapters in Greisheimer, Kimber et al., Reith et al., King & Showers, Chaffee & Greisheimer.

Materials:

1. Long bones from any small animal
2. 10% nitric acid
3. Oven

Objective: To demonstrate relationship of chemical composition to visible characteristics.

Procedure:

1. Soak one bone in 10% nitric acid for 24 hours. This removes all the inorganic salts (decalcification). Is the bone flexible or brittle? _____

2. Bake the other bone in an oven (250° F.) for 2 hours or until charred. Baking removes all the organic constituents of the bone. Is the bone flexible or brittle? _____

3. Discuss the characteristics of bone attributable to inorganic salts and organic substances. How do they differ? _____

_____

_____

_____

PRACTICAL EXERCISE

ANATOMY AND PHYSIOLOGY QUESTIONS

1. Name the chief sites of blood cell production in adults: _____

_____

_____

_____

_____

2. Name as many of the facial bones as you can feel on yourself. There are three pairs and one single: _____

_____

_____

_____

_____

3. Name the only bones which do not function in movement or protection of the body: _____

_____

_____

_____

CLINICAL QUESTIONS

1. Briefly define the following terms:
   a. Craniotomy: _____

   _____

   _____

   b. Sinusitis: _____

   _____

   _____

   c. Lordosis: _____

   _____

   _____

   d. Scoliosis: _____

   _____

   _____

   e. Kyphosis: _____

   _____

   _____

f. Spina bifida: _____

_____

_____

g. Osteoporosis: _____

_____

_____

2. What value does a sternal puncture have in diagnosing anemia? _____

_____

_____

3. Discuss the difference between a simple and depressed skull fracture.

_____

_____

_____

Chapter 6

THE ARTICULAR SYSTEM

The term "joint" refers to an articulation between cartilages or bones. Three general types are recognized: (1) immovable joints (synarthroses); (2) slightly movable joints (amphiarthroses); and (3) freely movable joints (diarthroses).

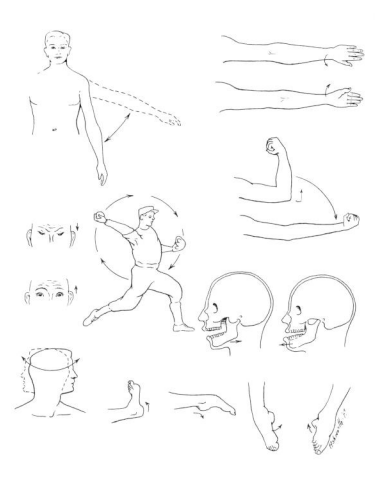

ANATOMY OF THE ARTICULAR SYSTEM
EXPERIMENT A: Comparison of Three Types of Articulations
EXPERIMENT B: Examination of Beef or Pig Knee Joint

PHYSIOLOGY OF THE ARTICULAR SYSTEM
EXPERIMENT C: Joint Movements
PRACTICAL EXERCISES

ANATOMY OF THE ARTICULAR SYSTEM

EXPERIMENT A: Comparison of Three Types of Articulations

References:
> J & F, Ch. 6; appropriate chapters in Greisheimer, Kimber et al., Anthony, Reith et al., King & Showers, Chaffee & Greisheimer (good x-rays).

Materials:
> 1. Articulated and disarticulated skeleton
> 2. X-ray films of joint areas (if available)

Objective: To demonstrate the differences in structure and function of articulations.

Procedure:
1. Using the references indicated above, examine x-rays and the articulated and disarticulated skeleton.
   a. Compare the suture of the skull to the pubic symphysis.
   b. Compare shoulder, hip, or knee joint to sutures of skull and the pubic symphysis.
   c. Note the differences in the degree of movement permitted by sutures of skull, pubic symphysis, and shoulder, hip, or knee joint.
2. List under the appropriate heading examples of each type of joint:
   a. Diarthroses

   (1) Ball and socket: _____

   (2) Hinge: _____

   (3) Condyloid: _____

(4) Pivot: _____

(5) Gliding: _____

b. Synarthroses: _____

c. Amphiarthroses

(1) Symphysis: _____

(2) Syndesmosis: _____

EXPERIMENT B: Examination of Beef or Pig Knee Joint

References:

   J & F, Ch. 6; appropriate chapters in Kimble et al., King & Showers.

Materials:

   Two beef or pig knee joints sawed in half. Saw one joint in a midcoronal plane and the other midsagittally to provide different aspects of the interior of the joint.

Objective: To demonstrate gross structure of a joint.

Procedure:

   1. Using references indicated above examine joints and find the following structures:

Articular cartilage	Ligaments
Ligamentous Capsule	Synovial membrane
Synovial cavity	Synovial fluid
	Patella (if present)

   2. Label Figures 25 and 26 from the terms given below:

Suprapatellar bursa	Quadriceps tendon
Prepatellar bursa	Patella
Infrapatellar bursa	Ligament of patella
Tibia	Fibula
Popliteus tendon	Lateral ligament
Femur	Tibial condyle
Capsule	Lateral gastrocnemius bursa
Bone marrow	Epiphyseal line
Deltoid muscle	Synovial membrane
Subdeltoid bursa	Joint cavity
Acromion	Articular cartilage
Clavicle	Scapula
Articular Capsule	Subacromial bursa
Supraspinatus muscle	

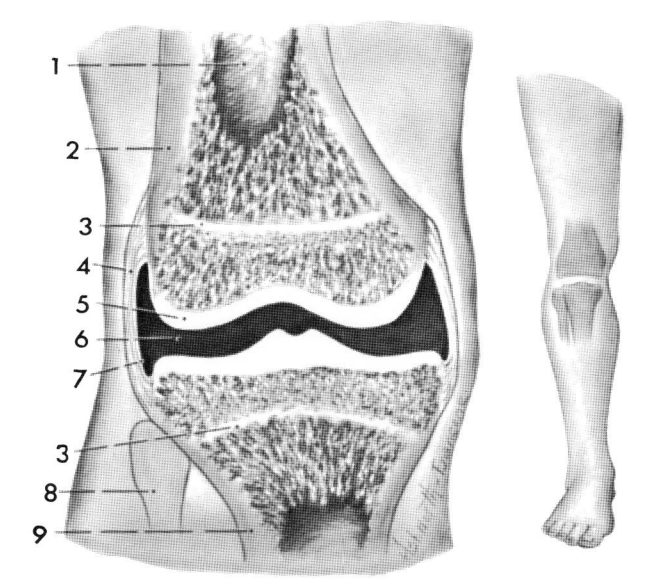

Figure 25. Anterior view of the knee joint.

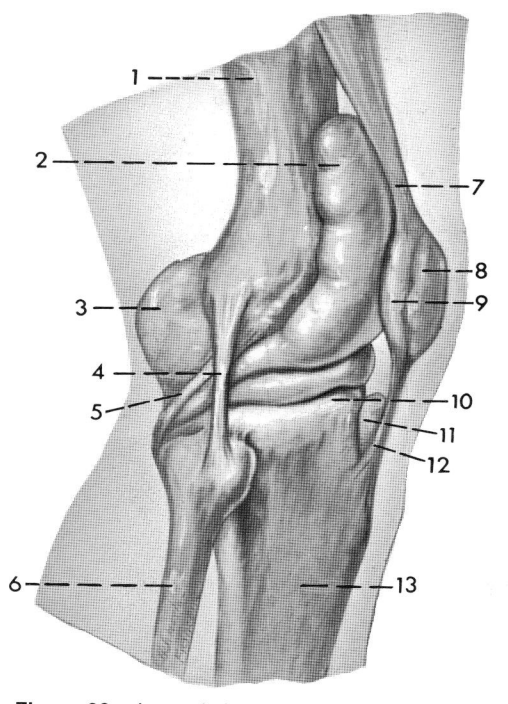

Figure 26. Lateral view of the right knee joint.

PHYSIOLOGY OF THE ARTICULAR SYSTEM

EXPERIMENT C: Joint Movements

References:

J & F, Ch. 6; appropriate chapters in Greisheimer, Kimber et al., Anthony, Reith et al., King & Showers, Chaffee & Greisheimer.

Objective: To demonstrate types of joint movements.

Procedure:

1. Bend your arm so that fingers touch shoulder. This involves what movement at the elbow? _____

2. Now straighten it. Name the movement involved: _____

3. Standing with feet together move the right foot away from the left. Name this movement: _____

4. Turn your head from side to side. Name this movement: _____

5. Hold your hand straight out from the shoulder; move the hand in a circle. This movement is: _____

6. Stand with hand at side, palm toward midline. Turn palm forward. Which movement is this? _____

Now backward. What movement is this? _____

7. Sitting on the edge of a chair with legs straight in front of you, heels on the floor, turn the soles of your feet away from each other. Name this movement: _____

Now turn them toward each other. What movement is this? _____

8. With teeth gently closed, move jaw forward to produce overbite. Name this movement: _____

Now move jaw backward to exaggerate underbite. Which movement is this?

PRACTICAL EXERCISES

ANATOMY AND PHYSIOLOGY QUESTIONS

    1. Give two functions of the synovial fluid: _____

_____

_____

_____

_____

    2. Describe the function of the ligaments surrounding the joints: _____

_____

_____

_____

_____

    3. What is the function of articular discs? _____

_____

_____

_____

_____

    4. What is the function of bursae? _____

_____

_____

_____

_____

CLINICAL QUESTIONS

    1. Define bursitis: _____

_____

_____

_____

_____

    2. Define arthritis: _____

_____

_____

_____

_____

    3. Define tenosynovitis: _____

_____

_____

_____

_____

4. Describe a treatment common to all the above: _____

_____

_____

_____

_____

Chapter 7

THE MUSCULAR SYSTEM

The muscular system assists in most of the activities of the body. Muscles work with the skeletal system to make movement and respiration possible, enable the heart and arteries to pump blood throughout the body, and perform the important task of transport of foodstuffs through the digestive system. These are just a few of the many functions of the muscular system. Impairment of any function of this system can lead to illness and, if serious, even to death.

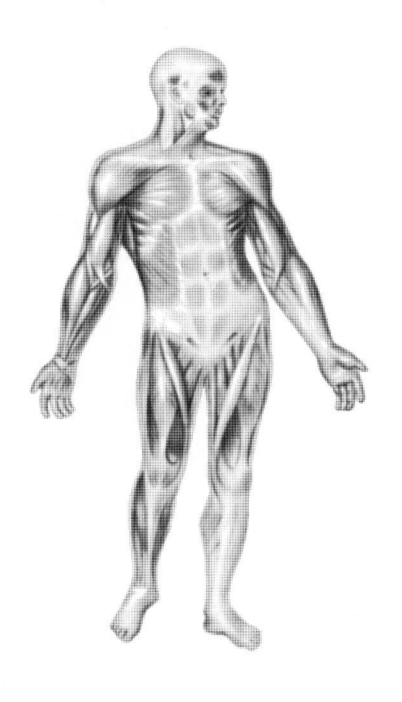

ANATOMY OF THE MUSCULAR SYSTEM
EXPERIMENT A: **Histology of Muscle**
EXPERIMENT B: **Dissection of Animal to Observe Muscles**
EXPERIMENT C: **Muscle Fiber**

PHYSIOLOGY OF THE MUSCULAR SYSTEM
EXPERIMENT D: **Skeletal Muscle Contraction**
EXPERIMENT E: **Activity of Intestinal Smooth Muscle (optional)**
EXPERIMENT F: **"All or None" Law (optional)**
EXPERIMENT G: **Relationship of Blood Supply to Muscle Fatigue**
PRACTICAL EXERCISES

ANATOMY OF THE MUSCULAR SYSTEM

EXPERIMENT A: Histology of Muscle

References:
J & F, Ch. 7; appropriate chapters in Greisheimer, Kimber et al., Reith et al., King & Showers, Dienhart, Chaffee & Greisheimer, Ham & Leeson. Any good histology book will illustrate cell structure by means of photomicrographs.

Materials:
1. Microscope
2. Histologic sections of muscle (smooth, striated, cardiac)

Objective: To correlate the structure of muscle with its various functions.

Procedure:
1. Using the references indicated above, examine prepared slides of the three types of muscle (smooth, striated, cardiac). Find the following structures.

Smooth involuntary
Smooth muscle fiber (cell)

      Cytoplasm
      Nucleus (single)
      Nucleolus
      Intercellular substance
    Striated voluntary (skeletal)
      Skeletal muscle fiber (cell)
      Cytoplasm
      Nucleus (a fiber is multinucleated)
      Endomysium
      Striations: A bands (dark), I bands (light)
    Striated involuntary (cardiac)
      Cardiac muscle fiber (cell)
      Cytoplasm
      Endomysium
      Nucleus (single)
      Intercalated disks
2. Label structures on Figure 27.

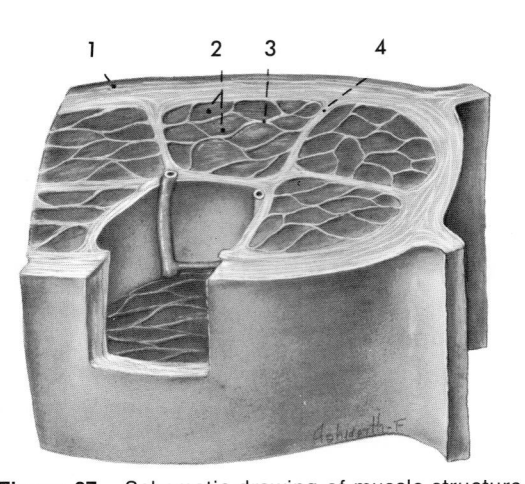

Figure 27. Schematic drawing of muscle structure.

3. Label Figs. 28 and 29 with the following terms:

Tendon   Perimysium
Epimysium   Endomysium
Individual muscle fiber   Bundle of muscle fibers

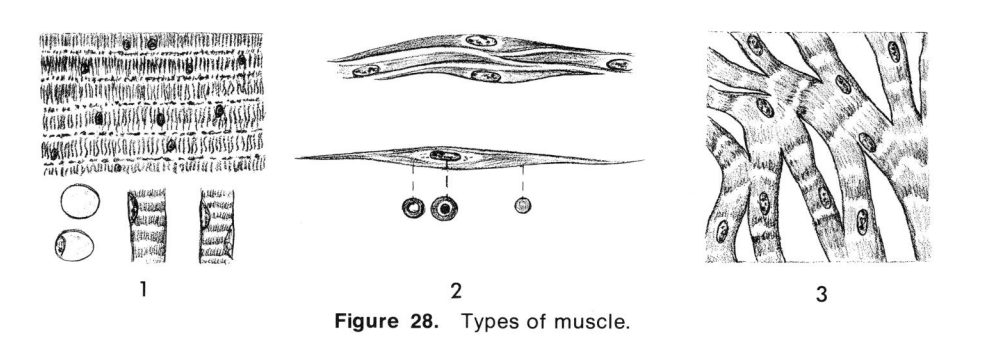

1   2   3

Figure 28. Types of muscle.

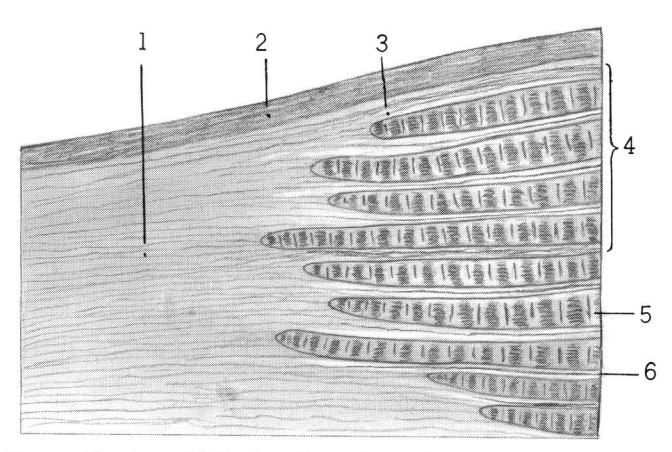

Figure 29. Longitudinal section of muscle terminating in tendon.

EXPERIMENT B: Dissection of Animal to Observe Muscles

References:

See appropriate animal dissection guide, p. 253. J & F, Ch. 7; appropriate chapters in Greisheimer, Anthony, Reith et al., King & Showers, Chaffee & Greisheimer.

Materials:

1. Laboratory animal (preserved)
2. Dissection instruments and tray

Objective: To demonstrate muscles.

Procedure:

1. With the animal on its back, make a longitudinal midventral incision from the neck to the pubic region.

2. Cut through the skin on the ventral side of each limb from the midsagittal incision to the ankles and wrists.

3. Make a circular cut around the neck, wrists, ankles, and base of tail.

4. Remove the skin: gradually loosen the skin from the body by cutting through the loose layer of superficial fascia or connective tissue. Observe the numerous small blood vessels passing to and from the skin.

5. Keep the animal moist.

6. Using an appropriate animal reference book, find as many muscles as your instructor directs.

7. Label Figures 30 and 31 with the following terms:

Sternocleidomastoid m.	Cephalic vein
Platysma m.	Nipple
Deltoid m.	Clavicle
Pectoralis m.	Serratus anterior m.
Latissimus dorsi m.	External oblique m.
Short head biceps brachii m.	Fascia of rectus abdominis m.
Long head biceps brachii m.	Linea semilunaris
Lateral head of triceps m.	Anterior superior iliac spine
Spermatic cord	Tensor fasciae latae
Great or long saphenous v.	Sartorius m.
Rectus femoris m.	Superficial inguinal ring
Penis	Saphenous opening
Scrotum	Trapezius m.
Vastus lateralis m.	Iliac crest
Suspensory ligament of penis	Medial border of scapula and auscultatory triangle
Umbilicus	Infraspinatus m.
Gracilis m.	Teres minor m.
Iliotibial tract	Teres major m.
Adductor magnus m.	Triceps m.
Semitendinous m.	Lumbar triangle
Biceps femoris m.	Fascia of gluteus medius m.
Fold of buttock	Gluteus medius
Iliac crest	Spine of scapula
Levator scapulae	

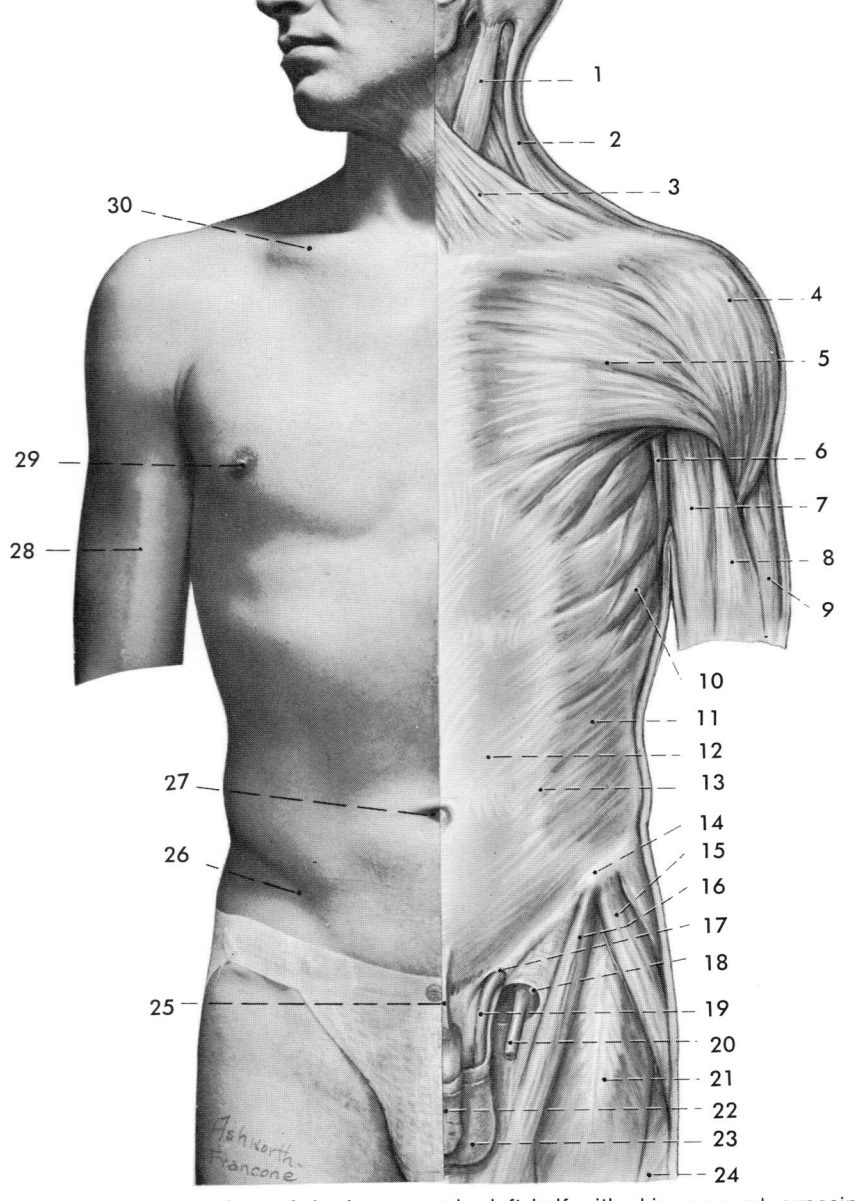

Figure 30. Anterior surface of the human male; left half with skin removed, exposing first muscle layer.

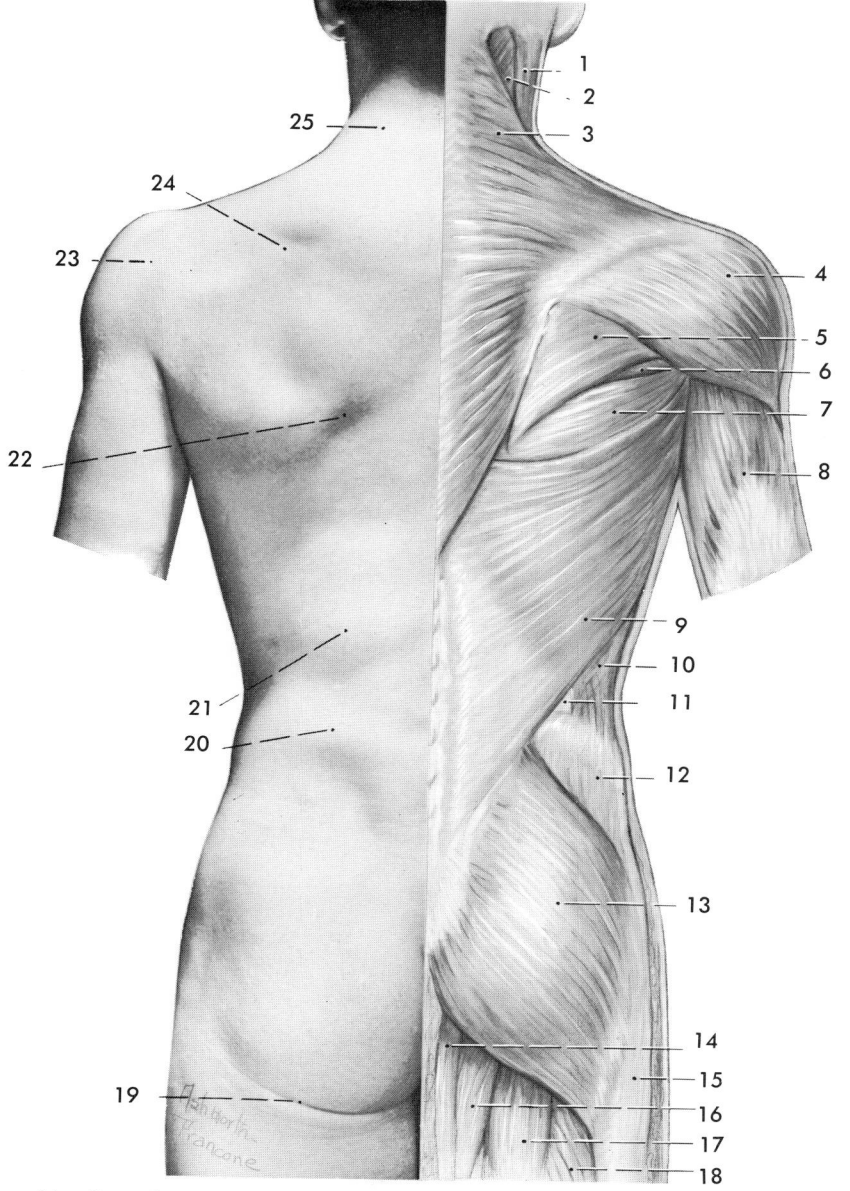

Figure 31. Posterior surface of the human male; right half with skin removed, exposing first muscle layer.

8. Label Figure 32 with the following terms:
   Anterior superior iliac spine   Vastus lateralis
   Sartorius m.   Lateral head of gastrocnemius
   Rectus femoris m.   Patella
   Biceps femoris m.

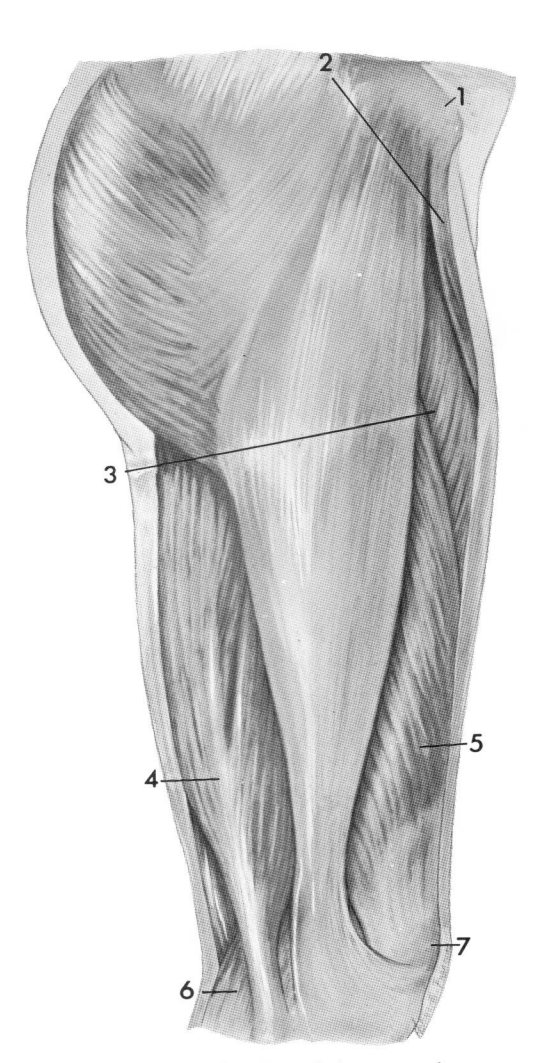

Figure 32. Muscles of the upper leg.

9. Label Figure 33 with the following terms:

Semitendinosus m.
Head of fibula
Tibialis anterior m.
Extensor digitorum longus m.
Peroneus longus m.
Soleus m.
Gastrocnemius m.

Peroneus brevis m.
Peroneus tertius m.
Tendo calcaneus
Abductor digiti minimi m.
Extensor hallucis longus m.
Extensor digitorum brevis m.

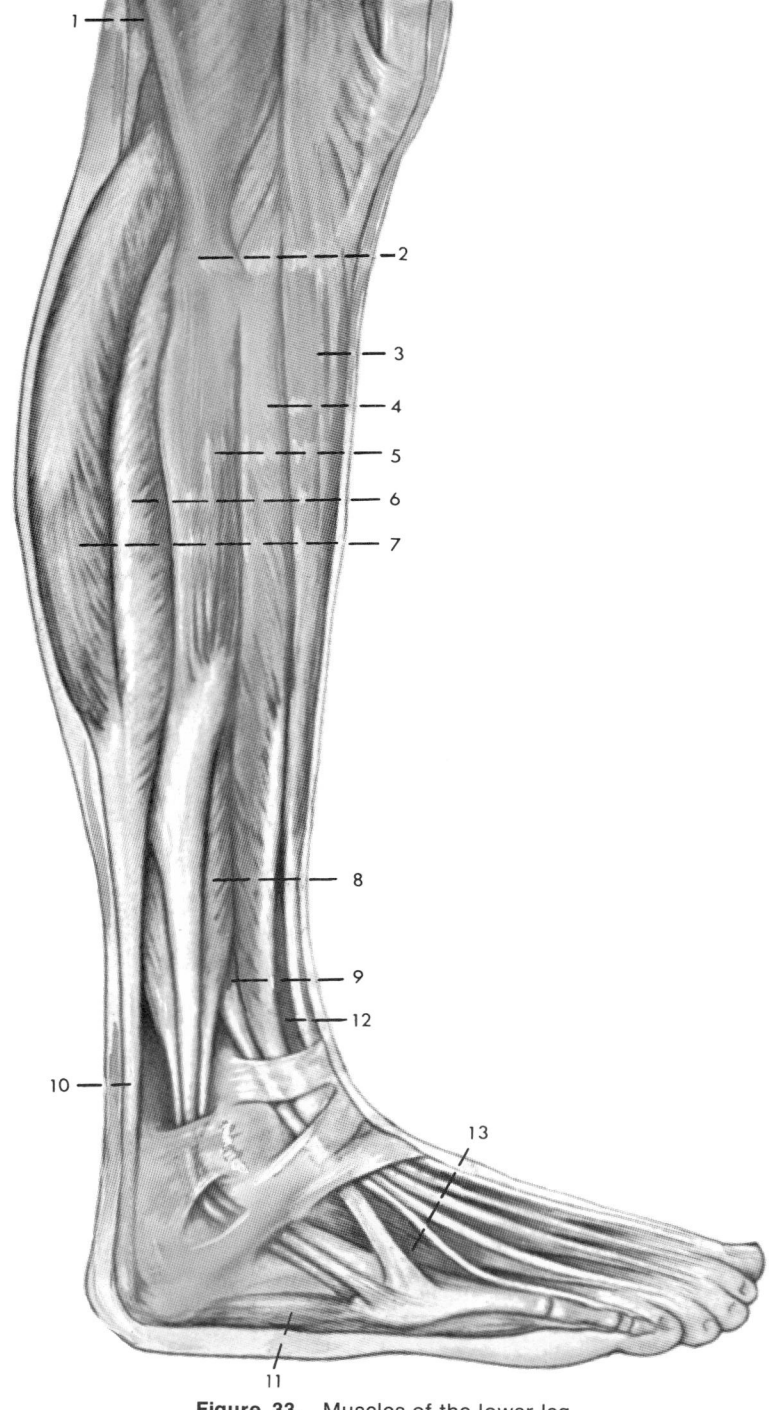

Figure 33. Muscles of the lower leg.

EXPERIMENT C: Muscle Fiber

References:

J & F, Ch. 7; appropriate chapters in Greisheimer, Kimber et al., Reith et al., King & Showers, Chaffee & Greisheimer.

Materials:

1. Muscle from animal dissected in preceding experiment
2. Needle probe
3. Slides
4. Microscope

Objective: To note relationship of fibers in a bundle of muscle.

Procedure:

1. Remove one of the muscles from the dissected animal and tease it apart until you have separated one fiber from the rest. Mount the fiber on a slide and examine it under the microscope. This fiber is one of many contained in a muscle bundle; it contains fibrils which, in turn, contain microfibers. The student should be able to identify the fibrils. The microfibers are visible only under an electron miscoscope.

2. After examining the slide, label Figure 34 with the following:

Whole muscle bundle   Muscle microfiber
Muscle fibril   Muscle fiber

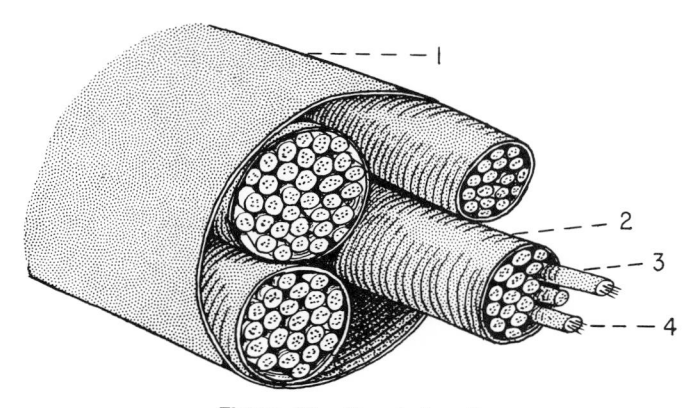

Figure 34. Muscle bundle.

PHYSIOLOGY OF THE MUSCULAR SYSTEM

EXPERIMENT D: Skeletal Muscle Contraction

References:

J & F, Ch. 7; appropriate chapters in Greisheimer, Kimber et al., Anthony, Guyton, Reith et al., King & Showers, Dienhart, Chaffee & Greisheimer.

Materials:

1. Kymograph and smoked drum
2. Frog
3. Dissecting instruments and tray
4. Normal saline (see appendix)
5. Gauze sponges
6. Inductorium (see Fig. 35B) or electronic stimulator

Objective: To demonstrate muscle contraction.

Procedure:

1. To insure having a fresh muscle preparation, first set up the apparatus present in your laboratory and then prepare the muscle.

2. Anesthetize a frog (follow procedure in Chapter 1, Experiment C). Kill frog by excising head.

3. Using scissors cut skin completely around the leg at the foot.

4. Insert a fine wire through the belly of the tendon of Achilles (use sharp needle or a pin hook). Cut tendon below wire.

5. With forceps lift the tendon and with scissors cut the fascia binding the gastrocnemius muscle to neighboring structures.

6. Cut away muscles from femur and, using scissors, cut the femur above the origin of the gastrocnemius muscle.

7. Sever tibia and fibula just below the knee.

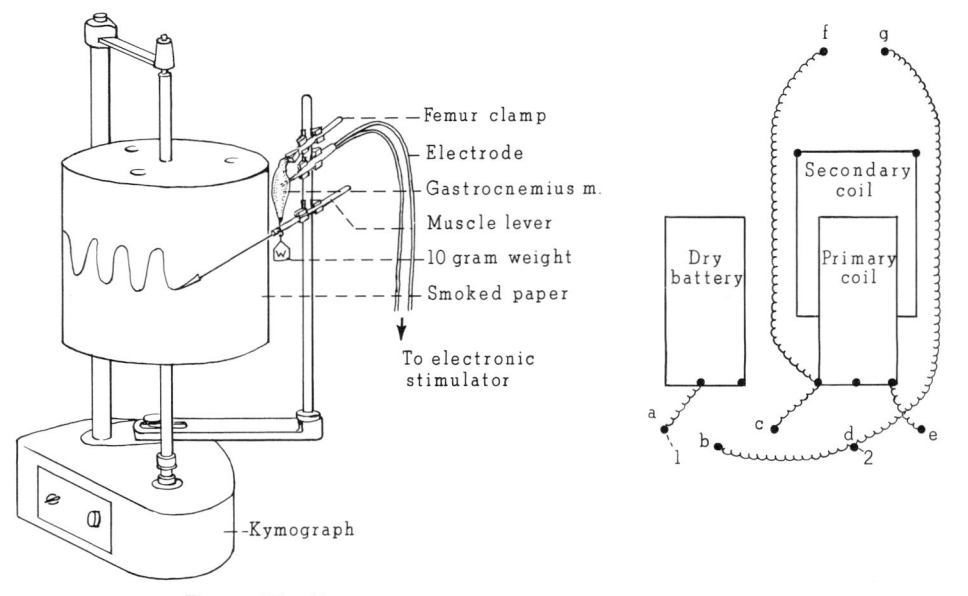

Figure 35. Kymograph for recording muscle contraction.

8. *Keep muscle preparation moist with normal saline at all times.*

9. Insert femur of the muscle preparation in jaws of muscle clamp and tie the thread of the tendon to the muscle level (keep muscle moist). Check to see if resting position of the muscle lever is horizontal.

10. Using a stimulus strength strong enough to produce maximal contraction, record a single muscle twitch.

11. a. Using different weights record several single muscle twitches.

b. Slowly and gradually increase the rate of stimulation to the muscle. Record incomplete tetanus, complete tetanus, and fatigue.

c. Use Fig. 36 to aid in recording the contractions.

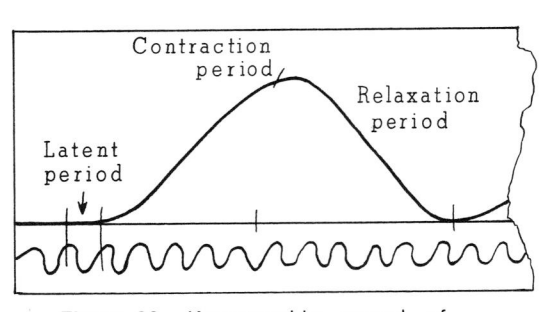

Figure 36. Kymographic record of skeletal muscle contraction.

EXPERIMENT E: Activity of Intestinal Smooth Muscle (optional)

References:

> J & F, Ch. 7; appropriate chapters in Greisheimer, Guyton, Chaffee & Greisheimer.

Materials:

1. Kymograph and smoked drum
2. Ringer's solution (see appendix)
3. 1¼ in. section of rabbit or other small animal intestine
4. Dry cells
5. Dissecting instruments and tray
6. Ring stand and clamps
7. Glass tubing
8. Wire hooks
9. Muscle lever
10. Beaker
11. Oxygen tank
12. Silk thread
13. 1:1000 adrenaline solution (see appendix)
14. 1:1000 acetylcholine solution (see appendix)
15. Locke's solution (see appendix)

Objective: Recording smooth muscle contractions.

Procedure:

1. To insure a fresh muscle preparation, set up the apparatus first (Fig. 37), and then prepare the intestinal muscle.

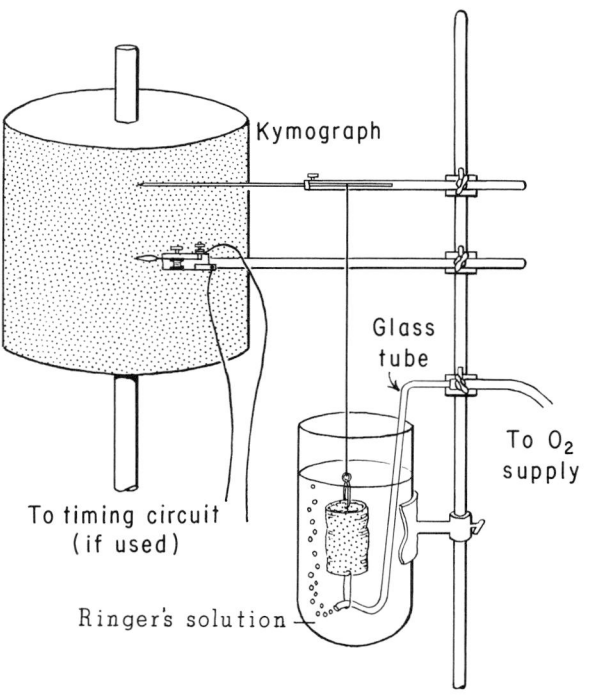

Figure 37. Kymograph setup for smooth muscle.

2. Obtain a 1¼ in. segment of small intestine from a freshly killed animal. Flush segment of small intestine thoroughly with Locke's solution twice. Fecal material must be removed.

3. Set up the experiment as seen in Figure 37.

    a. Fill test tube with Ringer's solution warmed to 38° C. The solution should contain glucose in a concentration of 100 mg. per 100 ml.

    b. Regulate the aeration so that fine bubbles issue through the solution and there will be little agitation of the muscle strip.

    c. Fasten the small segment of animal intestine with silk thread between the lever and air bubble L-tube. The upper end of the thread should be pressed into a bit of wax on the lever.

    d. It is important to ensure that the ends of the intestine remain open and that the recording lever is moderately weighted so as to stretch the muscle slightly.

4. Record the spontaneous contraction of the segment of intestine.

5. Add a few drops of 1:1000 adrenaline solution and record the contractions.

6. Wash preparation by replacing the bath with fresh, warmed Ringer's solution. Use a rubber syringe bulb to empty test tube. Add a few drops of 1:1000 acetylcholine solution and record the contractions.

7. Without washing, add double the dose of the 1:1000 acetylcholine solution found effective in 6.

8. Discuss your results and observations: _____

_____

_____

_____

_____

EXPERIMENT F: "All or None" Law (optional)

References:

J & F, Ch. 7; appropriate chapters in Greisheimer, Guyton, Reith et al., Chaffee & Greisheimer.

Materials:

1. Frog
2. Kymograph and smoked drum
3. Dissecting instruments and tray
4. Pithing needle
5. Ring stand
6. Lever
7. Ringer's solution (see appendix)
8. Hooks

Objective: To observe cardiac muscle action.

Procedure:

1. Set up apparatus first (Fig. 38).

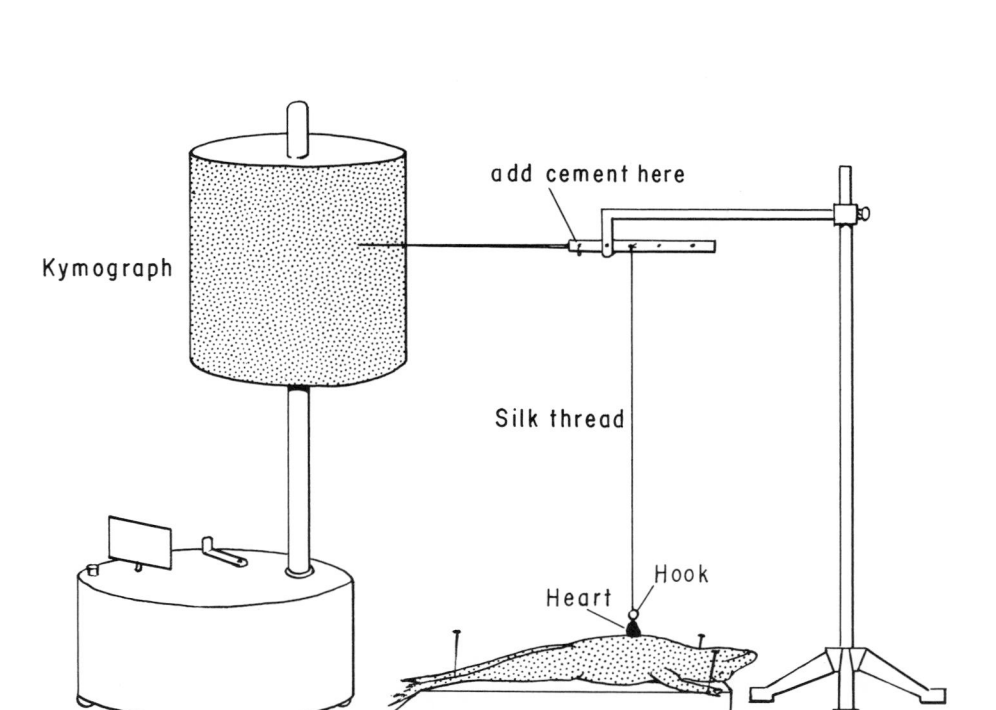

Figure 38. Kymograph setup for heart muscle in frog.

2. Pith brain of frog (Fig. 39). Hold frog in left hand with dorsal side up. With the index finger press nose down so that the head makes a right angle with the trunk. Feel for the slight depression betweeen the skull and spinal column by allowing the nail of your right index finger to glide down the head of the frog. This depression is about 3 mm. behind the line joining the posterior borders of the tympanic membranes. Insert a pithing needle into the median line of the groove (foramen magnum) and direct it forward and a little downward. Rotate it in the cranial cavity to destroy the brain. Allow time for recovery from neural shock.

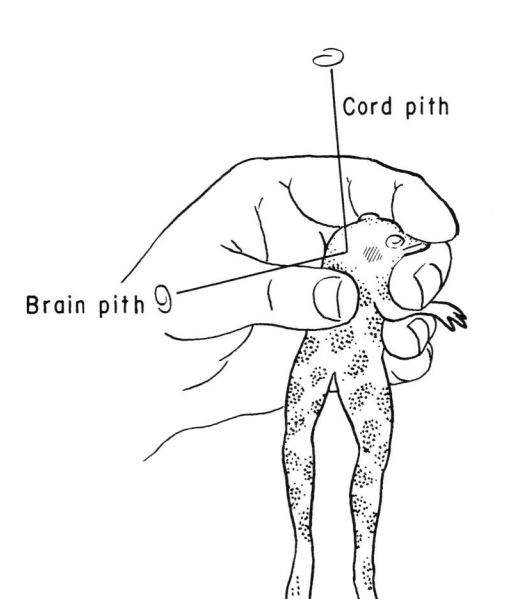

Cord pith

Brain pith

Figure 39. Correct procedure for pithing a frog.

3. Expose the heart by cutting through the sternum; remove the pericardium. Note that the frog heart is rhythmically relaxing (diastole) and then contracting (systole) in response to stimuli from the sinus venosus (heart pacemaker).

4. Put a fine hook through the apex of the heart, being careful not to puncture the ventricle. With thread connect the hook to the short arm of the heart lever. Do this by using wax or cement stuck to the short heart lever arm.

5. Apply Ringer's solution to the heart.

6. Raise heart from cavity of frog by applying a small quantity of cement on the long arm of the heart lever.

7. Make certain the thread between the heart and lever is vertical.

8. Record a normal frog heartbeat. Use Fig. 40 to aid in making your record.

9. Pass a ligature around the heart between the atrium and ventricle and increase the pressure to block the impulses from the pacemaker (heart block).

10. Pass two fine wires, connected to the secondary terminals of an induction coil, through two sides of the base of the ventricle (or use an electronic stimulator).

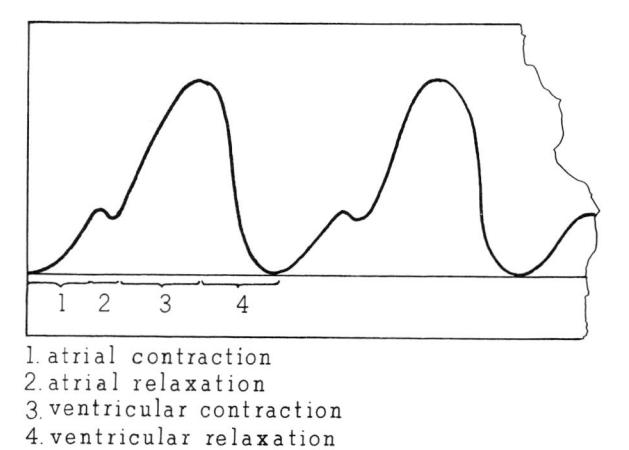

1. atrial contraction
2. atrial relaxation
3. ventricular contraction
4. ventricular relaxation

Figure 40. Kymographic record of cardiac activity.

11. Pull out the secondary coil as far as it will go and stimulate. Shorten the distance between the primary and secondary coils, stimulating at each setting until the heart muscle responds to the break stimulus.

12. Stimulate with a stronger break shock. Continue to increase the stimulus, allowing 20 seconds between each stimulation. Is the height of contraction increased? _____

13. Explain your results: _____

_____

_____

_____

_____

_____

_____

EXPERIMENT G: Relationship of Blood Supply to Muscle Fatigue

References:

J & F, Ch. 7; appropriate chapters in Greisheimer, Kimber et al., Anthony, Guyton, Reith et al., King & Showers, Chaffee & Greisheimer.

Procedure:

1. Rest forearm on table. Take ball and squeeze with fingers at a rate of about two contractions per second. Do this until fatigued. Allow a period of rest to permit recovery of muscles. Next apply blood pressure cuff. Inflate the cuff until you can no longer hear pulse with stethoscope applied to antecubital aspect of elbow joint. Then squeeze ball as before and note the difference in time subject is able to squeeze ball.

2. How do you explain this difference? _____

_____

_____

_____

_____

PRACTICAL EXERCISES

ANATOMY AND PHYSIOLOGY QUESTIONS

    1. Differentiate between the origin and the insertion of a muscle: _____

_____

_____

_____

_____

    2. Name the three different types of muscle: _____

_____

_____

_____

_____

    3. Discuss the differences between isometric and isotonic muscle contraction: _____

_____

_____

_____

_____

    4. Discuss the relationship between blood supply and muscle fatigue:

_____

_____

_____

_____

CLINICAL QUESTIONS

    1. Briefly define the following.

      a. Muscle spasm: _____

_____

_____

      b. Fibrillation: _____

_____

_____

      c. Spastic paralysis: _____

_____

_____

      d. Muscle tone: _____

_____

_____

e. Muscle atrophy: _____

_____

_____

f. Tennis elbow: _____

_____

_____

g. Hiatus hernia: _____

_____

_____

2. What is a "cramp"? What is the best way to relieve this condition? _____

_____

_____

_____

_____

UNIT 3

INTEGRATION
AND METABOLISM

Chapter 8

THE NERVOUS SYSTEM

The nervous system is concerned with the integration and control of all body functions. In association with the endocrine system, it creates an awareness of the environment and allows the human body to respond with precision to environmental changes. This awareness of man's environment is made possible by a group of tissues composed of highly specialized cells possessing the characteristics of excitability and conductivity.

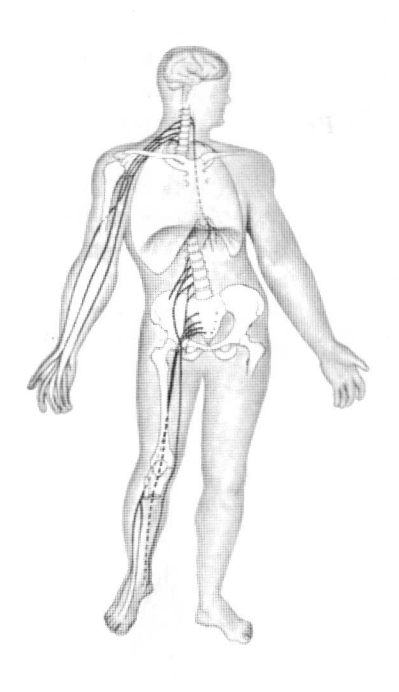

ANATOMY OF THE NERVOUS SYSTEM

EXPERIMENT A: Histology of Nervous Tissue
EXPERIMENT B: Human Brain
EXPERIMENT C: Preserved Sheep or Other Animal Brain and Meninges
EXPERIMENT D: Cranial Nerves
EXPERIMENT E: Spinal Cord and Spinal Nerves
EXPERIMENT F: Autonomic Nervous System

PHYSIOLOGY OF THE NERVOUS SYSTEM

EXPERIMENT G: Reflex Arc in the Frog
EXPERIMENT H: Reflex Arc in Man
EXPERIMENT I: Activities of a Normal, Spinal, and Decerebrate Frog (May be done as demonstration.)
EXPERIMENT J: Ascending and Descending Spinal Tracts (optional)
EXPERIMENT K: Referred Pain
EXPERIMENT L: Projection Areas of the Cerebral Cortex (optional)
EXPERIMENT M: Autonomic Effect of Adrenalin and Acetylcholine on Frog Eyes
PRACTICAL EXERCISES

ANATOMY OF THE NERVOUS SYSTEM

EXPERIMENT A: Histology of Nervous Tissue

References:
J & F, Ch. 8; appropriate chapters in Greisheimer, Kimber et al., Anthony, Reith et al., King & Showers, Dienhart, Chaffee & Greisheimer, Ham & Leeson. Any good histology book.
Materials: Histologic sections of nervous tissue
Objective: To observe the structural and physiological properties of nervous tissue.

Procedure:

1. Using the references indicated above, study slides of nervous tissue and identify the following structures:

Cell bodies of different types of neurons
Axons and dendrites of each type of neuron
Myelin sheath
Neurilemma
Nucleus
Nodes of Ranvier
Neurofibrils

2. Using references, indicate on Figures 41 and 42 the type of neuron illustrated and label with the following terms:

Dendrite	Muscle
Nucleus	Cell body
Myelin sheath	Axon
Node of Ranvier	Neurilemma
Nerve endings	Chromidial (Nissl) substance

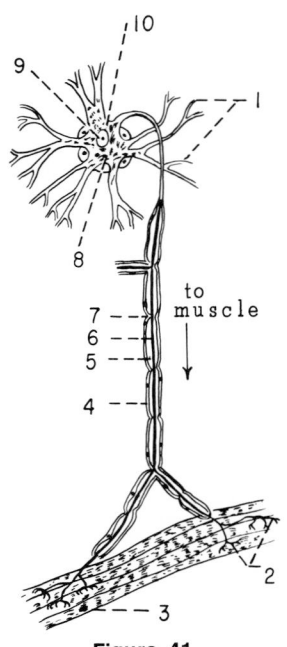

Figure 41.

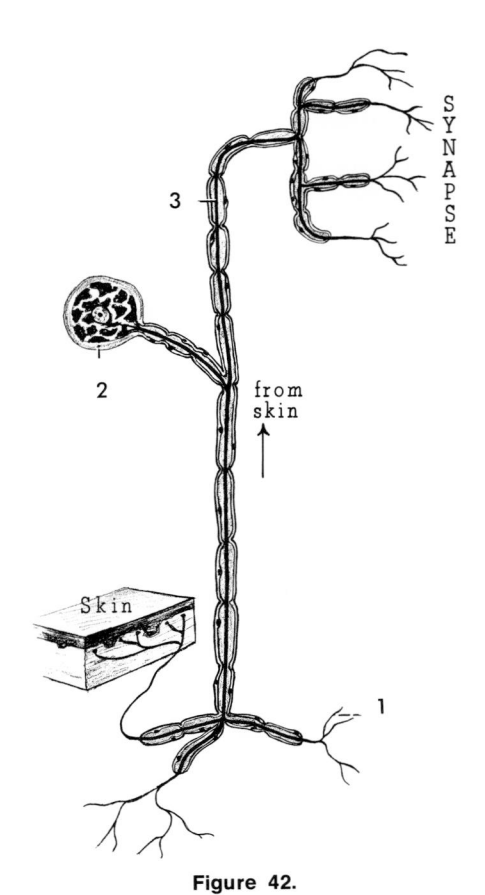

Figure 42.

3. Using references, label Figure 43 of a nerve in cross section with the following terms:

Endoneurium	Efferent neuron
Perineurium	Motor endings
Epineurium	Muscle fiber
Fascicles	Node of Ranvier

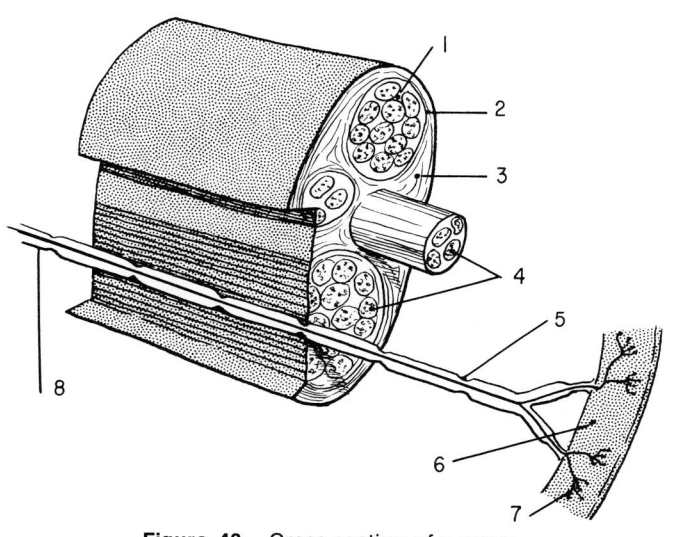

Figure 43. Cross section of a nerve.

EXPERIMENT B: Human Brain

References:

J & F, Ch. 8; appropriate chapters in Greisheimer, Kimber et al., Anthony, Reith et al., King & Showers, Dienhart, Chaffee & Greisheimer.

Materials:

1. Model of human brain with removable parts

2. Preserved human brain (intact, plus sagittal and coronal sections if available)

Objective: To observe the structural characteristics of the human brain.

Procedure:

1. Using the references indicated above, examine illustrations, model of human brain, and preserved human brain; read the text and identify the following:

Cerebellum	Cerebral lobes (frontal, parietal, temporal, occipital)
Pons	
Medulla oblongata	Optic chiasm
Hypophysis and stalk (infundibulum)	Choroid plexus of lateral ventricle
Pineal body	Thalamus
Corpus callosum	Hypothalamus
Third ventricle	Internal capsule
Fourth ventricle	Spinal cord
Tela choroidea	Fornix
Lateral sulcus	Cerebral aqueduct (Sylvius)
Caudate nucleus	Olive
Claustrum	Flocculus
Optic tract	Mammillary body
Trigeminal n. (V)	Globus pallidus
Pyramidal tract	Putamen
Nucleus of olivary body	Anterior pillar of fornix
Decussation of pyramids	Midbrain

2. Label Figures 44 to 46 using the above terms.

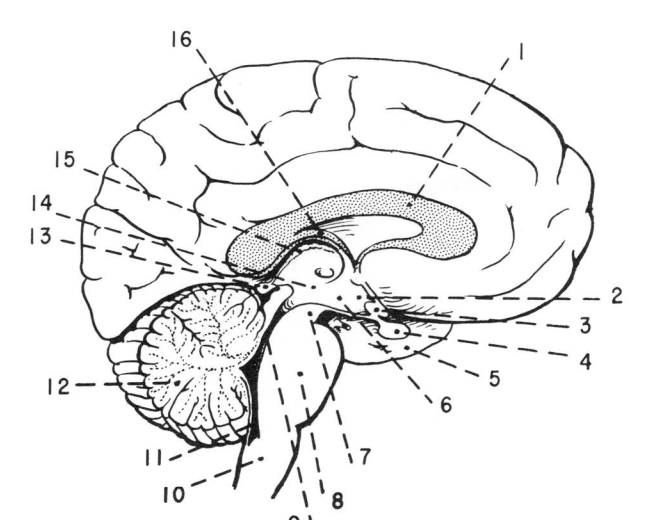

Figure 44. Sagittal view of the left half of the brain.

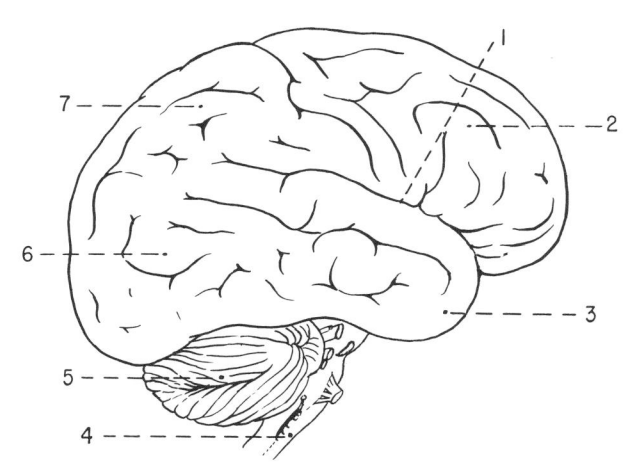

Figure 45. Right half of the brain.

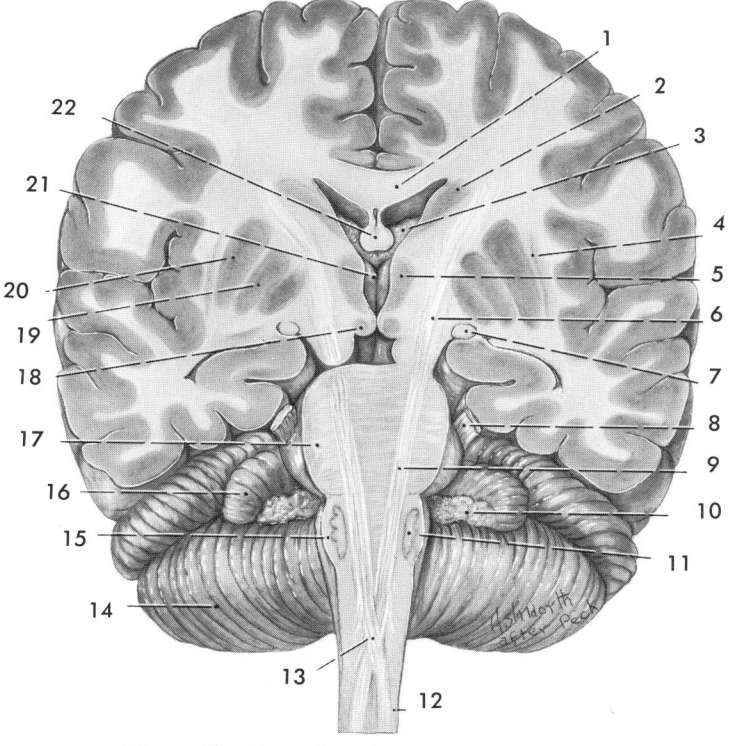

Figure 46. Frontal section through the brain.

EXPERIMENT C: Preserved Sheep or Other Animal Brain and Meninges

References:

J & F, Ch. 8; appropriate animal dissection guide (see appendix); appropriate chapters in Greisheimer, Kimber et al., Anthony, Reith et al., King & Showers, Dienhart, Chaffee & Greisheimer.

Materials:

1. Preserved sheep or other animal brain with meninges intact
2. Dissecting instruments and tray

Procedure:

1. Before dissection, observe the brain from above, identifying the following with the aid of the references indicated.

Dura mater	Arachnoid (vascular)
Falx cerebri	Pia mater
Tentorium cerebelli	

2. Examine the base of the brain; identify the following:

Olfactory bulbs	Hypophysis
Optic chiasm	Trigeminal nerves
Optic nerves	

3. Remove the dura mater by cutting through the tentorium cerebelli and then gently pulling the entire membrane free of the brain. The hypophysis may also be removed. Identify the following:

Cerebrum	Pons
Cerebellum	Medulla oblongata
Midbrain	Sulci and gyri

Major fissures:
  Longitudinal and transverse
  Lateral (Sylvius) and central (Rolando)
Lobes of cerebrum:
  Frontal and parietal
  Temporal and occipital
Cranial nerves

4. Gently separate the parietal lobes along the longitudinal fissure until you see the band of white fibers connecting the cerebral hemispheres. Using a sharp scalpel, make a midline incision through the remainder of the cerebrum, brain stem, cerebellum, and spinal cord.

Looking at the interior of the brain, identify the following:

Corpus callosum	Pineal body
Lateral ventricles	Aqueduct of Sylvius
Choroid plexus	Fourth ventricle
Foramen of Monro	Cerebellum and arbor vitae
Third ventricle	Midbrain
Thalamus	Pons

5. Make a coronal (frontal section) of one cerebral hemisphere in the region of the thalamus and identify the following:

Cortex	Thalamus and alternate stripes
Corpus callosum	of gray and white matter
Lateral ventricle	Interior of cerebrum

EXPERIMENT D: Cranial Nerves

References:

J & F, Ch. 8; Greisheimer, Kimber et al., Anthony, Reith et al., King & Showers, Dienhart, Chaffee & Greisheimer.

Materials:

1. Preserved human or animal brain with cranial nerves intact if possible

2. Model of brain

Objective: To observe location and function of cranial nerves.

Procedure:

1. Using the references indicated above, examine models and preserved brains; note the points at which the various cranial nerves arise from the base of the brain. Label Figure 47 using the name and number of each cranial nerve.

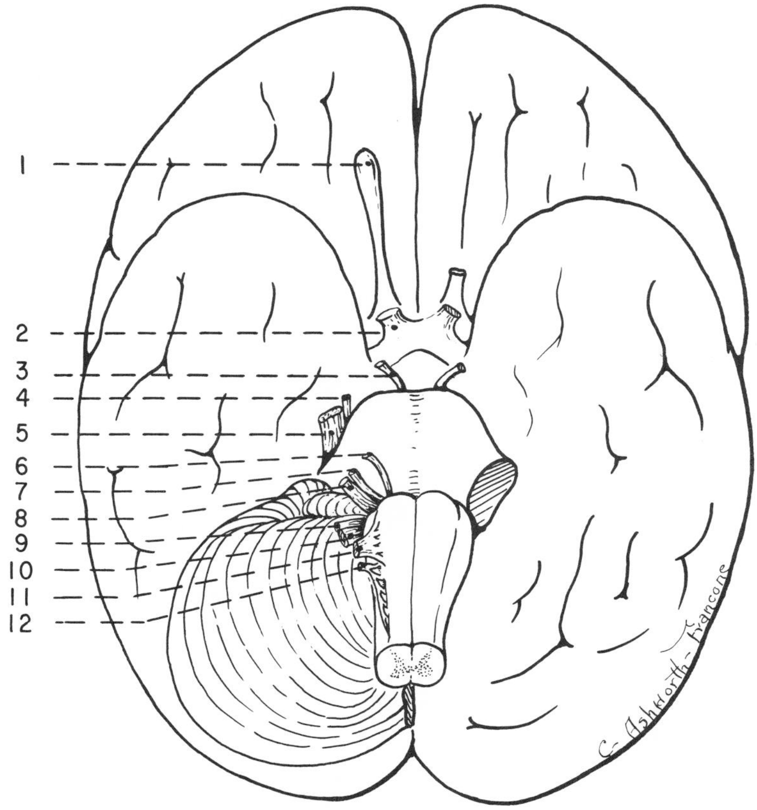

Figure 47. Inferior surface of the brain.

a. Which cranial nerves are described as sensory nerves? Give name
and function. _____

_____

_____

_____

b. Which cranial nerves are described as motor nerves? Give name
and function. _____

_____

_____

_____

c. Which cranial nerves are mixed? _____

_____

_____

_____

EXPERIMENT E: Spinal Cord and Spinal Nerves

References:

J & F, Ch. 8; Greisheimer, Kimber et al., Anthony, Reith et al., King & Showers, Dienhart, Chaffee & Greisheimer.

Materials:

1. Embalmed cat (demonstration)
2. Preserved human spinal cord (if available)
3. Models and illustrations of cross section of human spinal cord
4. Charts of spinal nerve and peripheral branches

Objective: To observe the anatomic features that characterize the spinal cord and spinal nerves.

Procedure

1. Using the references indicated above, examine a preserved human spinal cord, models and illustrations of the cross section of the human cord, charts of spinal nerve branches to the periphery, and the embalmed cat. Identify the following:

> Distribution of gray and white matter
> Anterior and posterior columns of gray matter
> Anterior, lateral, and posterior funiculus of white matter
> Central canal
> Dorsal and ventral roots of spinal nerves
> Spinal ganglia

2. Using the references, label Figures 48 and 49 with the following
terms:

Central canal

Anterior median fissure

Posterior column (horn) of
   gray matter

Posterior and anterior
   longitudinal lig.

Vertebral arteries and veins

Dorsal primary ramus

Anterior column (horn) of
   gray matter

Dorsal root

Dorsal root ganglion

Spinal nerve

Meningeal coverings

Vertebral canal

Dura mater

Ventral root

Ventral primary ramus

Spinal ganglion

Posterior funiculi

Anterior funiculus

Lateral funiculus

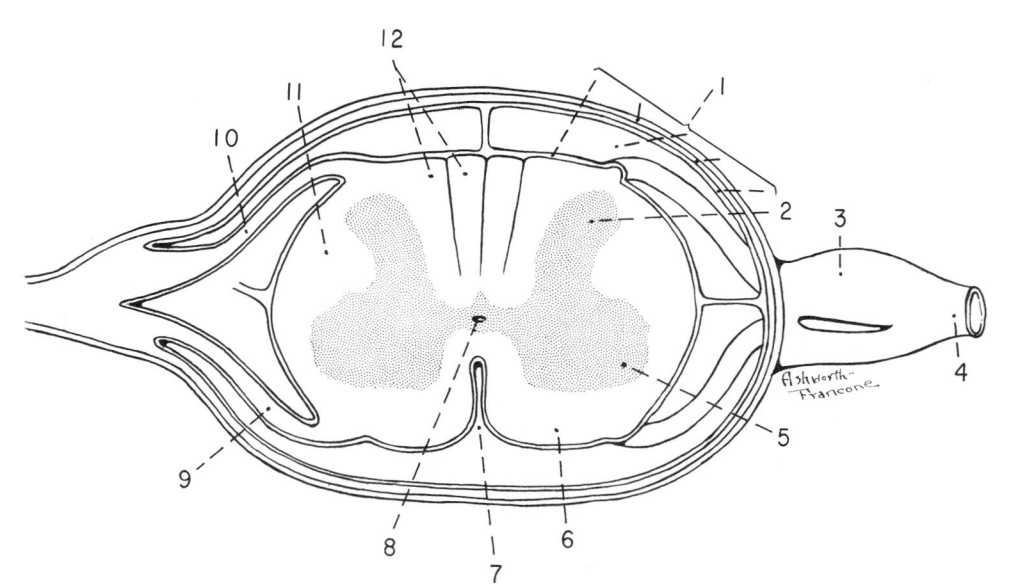

Figure 48. Cross section of the spinal cord.

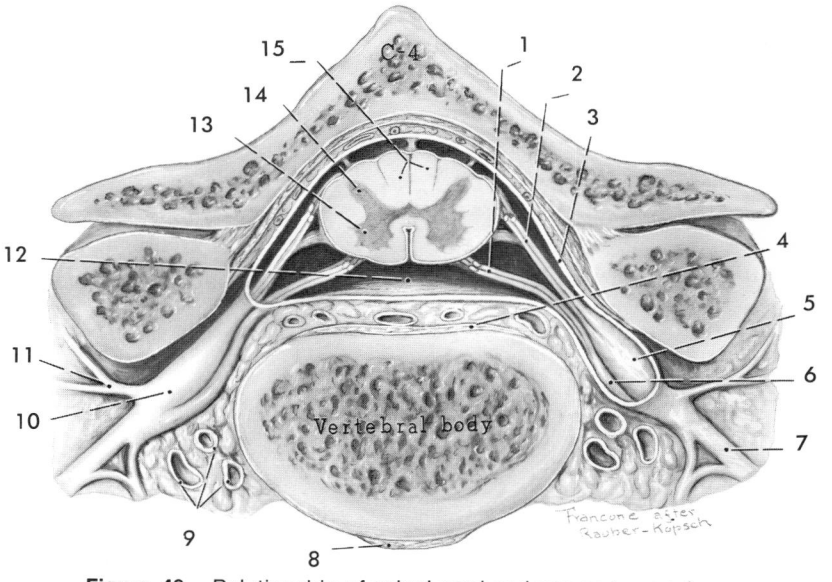

Figure 49. Relationship of spinal cord and nerves to vertebrae.

EXPERIMENT F: Autonomic Nervous System

References:

J & F, Ch. 8; appropriate chapters in Greisheimer, Kimber et al., Anthony, Guyton, Reith et al., King & Showers, Dienhart, Chaffee & Greisheimer.

Materials:

1. Illustration of autonomic nervous system
2. Embalmed cat (demonstration)

Objective: To understand the function of the autonomic nervous system.

Procedure:

1. Study the references on the autonomic nervous system; then examine the illustrations and the dissected embalmed cat. On Figure 50 draw in the following using colored pencils: preganglionic (black) and postganglionic fibers (sympathetic—blue; parasympathetic—red) to show the thoracolumbar and craniosacral innervation of the structures to the right of the nerve cord.

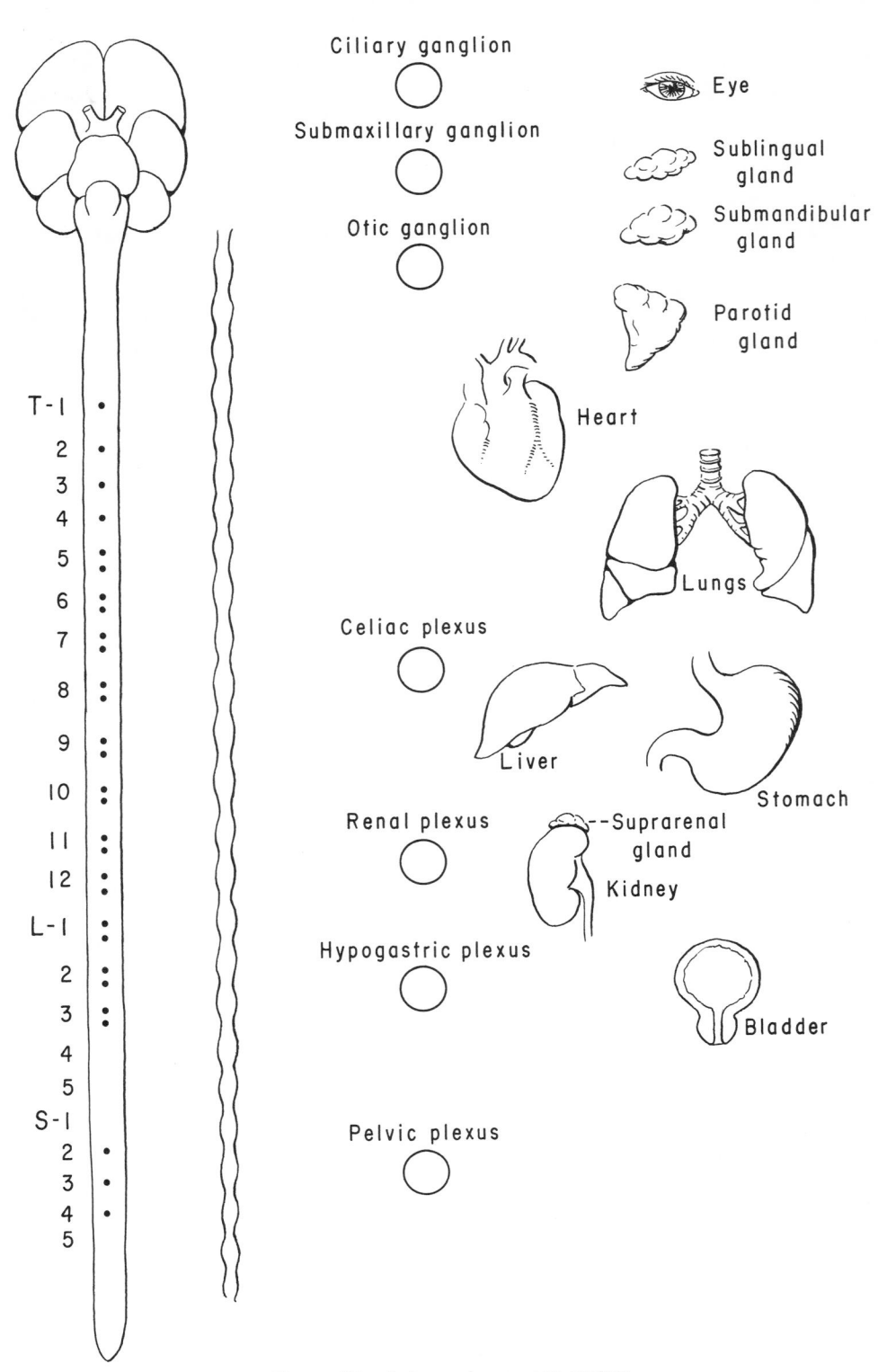

Figure 50. Autonomic nervous system.

PHYSIOLOGY OF THE NERVOUS SYSTEM

EXPERIMENT G: Reflex Arc in the Frog

References:
> Appropriate chapters in Greisheimer, Kimber et al., Guyton, Reith et al., King & Showers.

Materials:
1. Frog
2. Dilute nitric or sulfuric acid
3. Dissecting instruments and tray
4. Cotton swabs
5. Two beakers
6. Pithing needle
7. Ring stands and burette clamp

Objective: To observe the structural characteristics functioning in a reflex arc.

Procedure:
1. Pith frog brain (follow procedure in Chapter 7, Experiment F).
2. Place frog dorsal side up on the moistened surface of your dissecting tray. Note its position. Straighten the hind legs. Does the frog flex them again?

_____

3. Suspend the frog from a ring stand by placing its lower jaw in a burette clamp. Fasten securely.

    a. Pinch the toe of one foot. Describe the response: _____

_____

    b. Gently extend the right leg, leaving the left leg in usual flexed position. Touch the toes of the right foot with a swab dipped in dilute nitric or sulfuric acid. Describe the response: _____

_____

_____

    c. Hold the toe so that the right foot cannot be withdrawn and pinch firmly. This demonstrates a crossed reflex. Response? _____

_____

    d. Without removing the frog from the ring stand, remove acid by rinsing the foot in a beaker of water. Apply acid to the dorsal body wall. Response? _____

_____

_____

    e. Remove acid with water as before. Apply acid to the ventral body wall. Response? _____

_____

_____

f. Remove the frog from the ring stand and slit the skin on the ventral surface on left thigh. Separate the muscles of the thigh to expose the sciatic nerve. Cut through this nerve. Replace the frog on the ring stand and touch the toes of left foot with swab dipped in dilute acid. Response? _____

_____

g. Remove frog and pith the cord; insert pithing needle into occipitovertebral junction as for pithing the brain, but this time move the needle downward into the spinal cavity and move it several times to destroy the cord. Result? _____

_____

_____

h. Touch toes of right foot with acid swab. Response? _____

_____

i. Save frog head for experiment M.

4. Label on Figures 51 and 52 the neurons which demonstrate a reflex arc. Label your drawing with the following terms:

Spinal cord   Internuncial neuron
Sensory neuron   Effector muscle
Receptor   Cell body of sensory neuron
Motor neuron   Dorsal root ganglion
Cell body of motor neuron   Ventral root

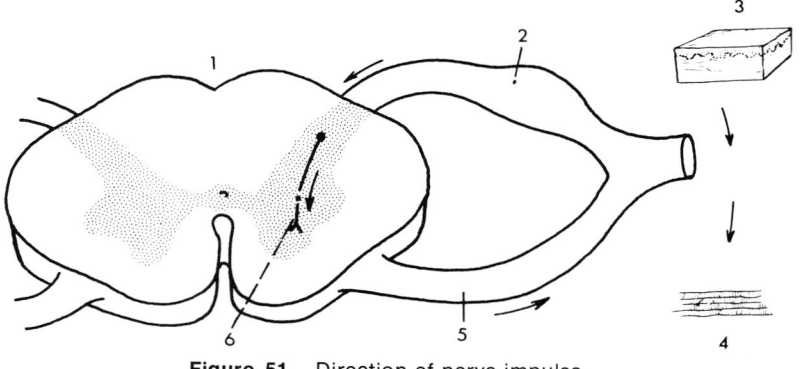

Figure 51. Direction of nerve impulse.

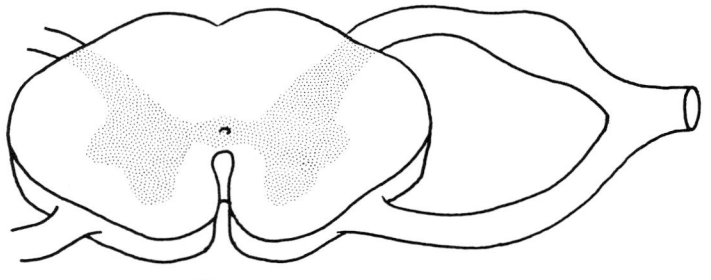

Figure 52. Simple reflex arc.

EXPERIMENT H: Reflex Arc in Man

References:
J & F, Ch. 8; appropriate chapters in Greisheimer, Kimber et al., Anthony, Guyton, Reith et al., King & Showers.

Materials:
1. Cotton
2. Flashlight
3. Rubber hammer

Objective: To observe different types of human reflex arcs.

Procedure:

1. Have a student sit down, cross his legs, relax, and close his eyes. Tap the skin over the patellar tendon with a rubber hammer or the edge of your hand. This is called the patellar reflex.

Describe what you observe: _____

_____

_____

2. Have a standing subject rest one knee on a chair. While you bend the foot to stretch the gastrocnemius muscle, tap the skin of the Achilles tendon with the edge of your hand or a rubber hammer. This is called the Achilles reflex.

Response? _____

_____

_____

3. Use a small piece of cotton twisted to a fine point and touch the edge of a student's cornea. This is called a corneal reflex.

Describe what you observe: _____

_____

_____

4. Have a student open his mouth. Using a wooden applicator with a wisp of cotton on its end, gently touch the uvula. This is called the pharyngeal reflex.

Response? _____

_____

_____

5. Stroke the short hair on the back of one side of a student's neck with your finger very gently; at the same time observe the size of the subject's pupil.

    a. Response when right side is stroked? _____

_____

    b. Response when left side is stroked? _____

_____

EXPERIMENT I: Activities of a Normal, Spinal, and Decerebrate Frog (May be done as demonstration)

References:
   Appropriate chapters in Greisheimer, Kimber et al., Anthony, Guyton, Reith et al., King & Showers, Chaffee & Greisheimer.
Materials:
   1. Dissecting instruments and tray
   2. Normal saline (see appendix)
   3. Ether or Nembutal
   4. Inductorium or electronic stimulator (see Fig. 35)
   5. Frogs (3)
Objective: To observe activities of frogs following nervous dissection.
Procedure:
   1. Using the references indicated above, learn the different parts of a frog brain.
   2. Anesthetize the first frog (follow procedure in Chapter 1, Experiment C). A preferred anesthetic is an intraperitoneal injection of ¼ cc. of Nembutal per 50 gm. of body weight.
   3. Cut the skin over the top of the skull along a line connecting the front margins of the two tympanic membranes. Next make a median incision forward to the nostrils. Lay back the skin flaps. Cut through the skull bone immediately in front of the transverse skin incision by carefully bringing the points of your scissors together on the top of the skull. Snip the bony covering of the cerebrum at one side. Do the same to the other side. Lift the bone with forceps and cautiously cut forward on both sides, exposing the cerebrum. Be careful not to injure the optic lobes. Using a sharp knife, cut the connection between the optic lobes and the cerebrum, and remove the cerebrum. Use silk thread to sew together the skin flaps. Note the posture of frog immediately after operation.
   4. Pith the brain of the second frog (follow procedure in Chapter 7, Experiment F). Note posture of the frog immediately after pithing.
   5. Keep skin of frogs moist.
   6. Perform the following experiments with a normal frog as control:
      a. Rotate each frog on a dissecting tray on turntable. Response of each frog? _____

      _____

      b. Check for limpness or rigidity in frogs. Result for each frog? _____

      _____

      c. Shock each frog with a mild tetanizing current and then put each in a tank or jar of water. Response of each frog as to control over direction of location? _____

      _____

      d. Place a light close to the eyes of each frog. Response as to blinking?

      _____

      _____

      _____

e. Observe respiratory movements. Respirations per minute of each frog? _____

_____

f. Place an obstacle in front of the frogs and stimulate with a mild tetanizing current. Do the frogs make attempts to jump over or around the obstacle? _____

_____

_____

EXPERIMENT J: Ascending and Descending Spinal Tracts (optional)

References:

J & F, Ch. 8; appropriate chapters in Greisheimer, Kimber et al., Anthony, Reith et al., King & Showers, Chaffee & Greisheimer.

Objective: To understand how sensory and motor fibers are organized in the spinal cord.

Procedure:

1. One of the functions of the spinal cord is to convey messages to and from the brain. This function is made possible via the ascending and descending spinal tracts.

2. Consult references and illustrations to learn the locations of ascending and descending spinal tracts. Label Figure 53 with the following terms:

White and gray commissure   Dorsal root
Apex of posterior column   Ventral root
Posterior gray commissure   Anterior column
Comma tract

Ascending Tracts   *Descending Tracts*
(Sensory Tracts)   *(Motor Tracts)*

Ventral spinothalamic tract   Tectospinal tract
Spinotectal tract   Lateral vestibulospinal tract
Spino-olivary tract   Corticospinal tract
Posterior spinocerebellar   Rubrospinal tract
  tract   Olivospinal tract
Funiculus cuneatus   Anterior corticospinal
Anterior spinocerebellar   tract
  tract   Anterior vestibulospinal tract
Funiculus gracilis
Lateral spinothalamic tract

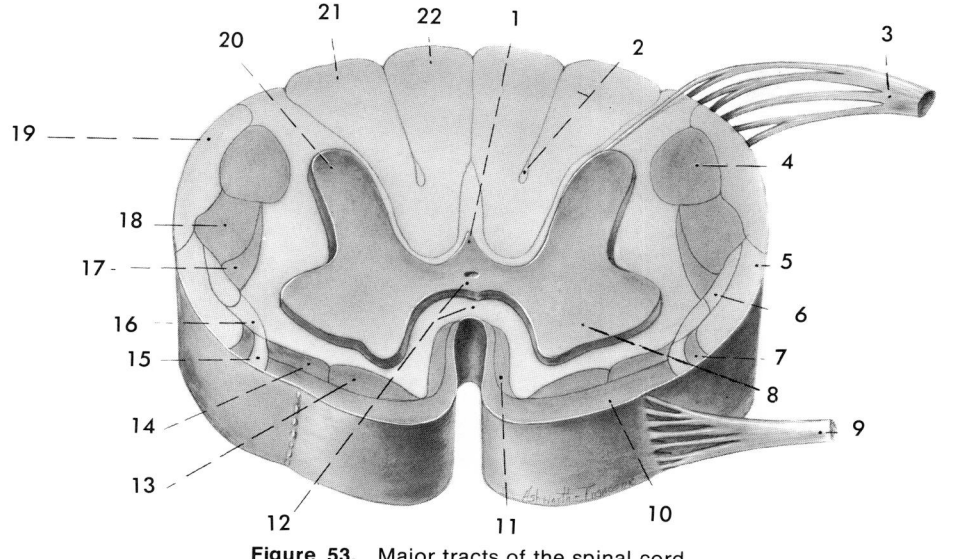

Figure 53. Major tracts of the spinal cord.

EXPERIMENT K: Referred Pain

References:

J & F, Ch. 8; appropriate chapters in Greisheimer, Anthony, Guyton, Chaffee & Greisheimer.

Procedure:

1. Place the tips of the fingers over the ulnar nerve at the elbow and move them back and forth while applying pressure. This should cause a slightly painful, tingling sensation.

a. Is the sensation referred to the elbow or to the hand? _____

_____

_____

b. What is referred pain? _____

_____

_____

2. Using the references, label the sites of referred pain in Figure 54 with the following terms:

Liver	Kidney
Appendix	Ovary
Right ureter	Small intestine
Bladder	Gallbladder
Colon	Stomach
Heart	

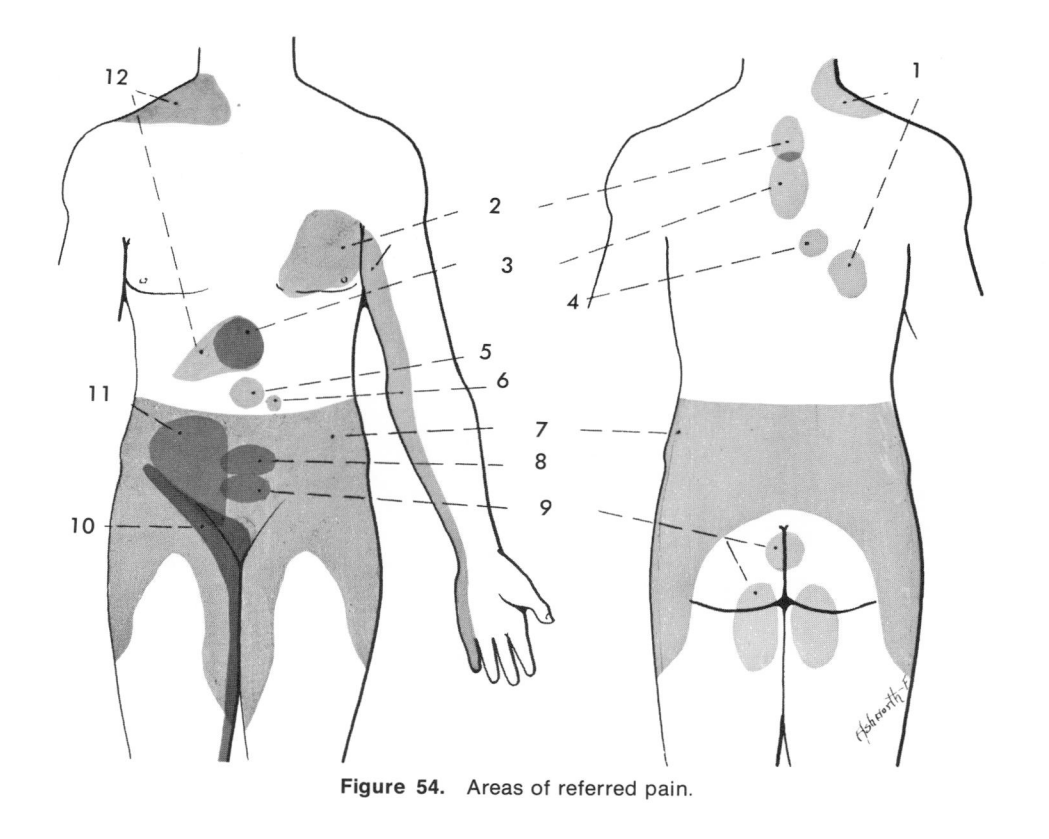

Figure 54. Areas of referred pain.

EXPERIMENT L: Projection Areas of the Cerebral Cortex (optional)

References:

J & F, Ch. 8; appropriate chapters in Greisheimer, Kimber et al.,
Anthony, Guyton, Reith et al., King & Showers, Chaffee & Greisheimer.

Materials:

Colored pencils

Procedure:

1. Using the references indicated above, learn the names and location
of the lobes of the cerebral cortex and place the following terms on the appropriate lines of Figure 55:

        Central sulcus (fissure of Rolando)
        Lateral sulcus (fissure of Sylvius)
        Cerebellum
        Color:
           Frontal lobe – blue
           Parietal lobe – red
           Temporal lobe – green
           Occipital lobe – yellow

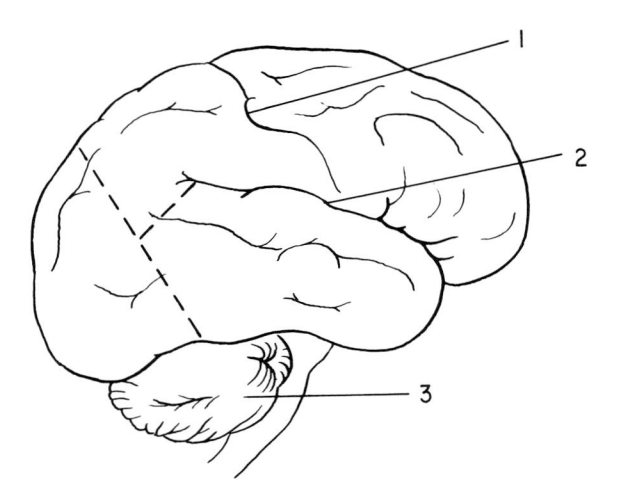

Figure 55. Lobes of the cerebral cortex.

2. Portions of the cerebral cortex that have become specialized for dispatch of motor directives and for reception of sensory messages are known as projection areas. Study the references concerned with projection areas and color the following on Figure 56:

> Visual area—purple stripes
> Auditory area—brown stripes
> Olfactory area—orange stripes
> Motor area—red stripes
> Sensory area—blue stripes
> Prefrontal area—black stripes

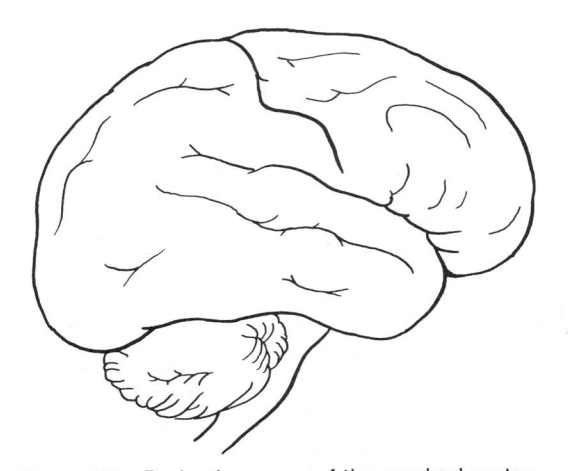

Figure 56.   Projection areas of the cerebral cortex.

EXPERIMENT M: Autonomic Effect of Adrenalin and Acetylcholine on Frog's Eyes

References:

Appropriate chapters in Greisheimer, Kimber et al., Anthony, Guyton, Reith et al., King & Showers, Chaffee & Greisheimer.

Materials:

1. Frog's eyes (2)
2. Acetylcholine solution, 5% (see appendix)
3. Adrenalin solution, 5% (see appendix)
4. Petri dishes or watch glasses
5. Dissecting instruments

Objective: To observe cholinergic and adrenergic effects on the autonomic nervous system.

Procedure:

1. Remove both eyes from a frog's head.
2. Clean eyes enough so that the pupils may be observed.
3. Place one eye in a 5% acetylcholine solution and the other in a 5% adrenalin solution.

    a. Response of pupil in 5% acetylcholine _____

    b. Response of pupil in 5% adrenalin _____

4. Reverse procedure 3 after washing the eyes in amphibian saline.

    a. Response of pupil in 5% acetylcholine _____

    b. Response of pupil in 5% adrenalin _____

5. Discuss your results. _____

_____

_____

_____

_____

PRACTICAL EXERCISES

ANATOMY AND PHYSIOLOGY QUESTIONS

1. Define: motor nerve; sensory nerve; mixed nerve; neuroglia cells.

_____

_____

_____

2. Describe the purpose of the meninges: _____

_____

3. Spinal nerves arise from the cord by two roots.

    a. Which contain afferent fibers? _____

       _____

    b. Which contain efferent fibers? _____

       _____

4. Describe acetylcholine; where is it formed? _____

5. Why does it take only a few seconds for the body to mobilize its reserves in case of an emergency but many minutes to "calm down" when the crisis is over? _____

_____

6. What is the pyramidal system? Describe its function. _____

_____

_____

_____

CLINICAL QUESTIONS

1. A lumbar puncture removes cerebrospinal fluid from what space? _____

_____

2. At what level is a lumbar puncture done? _____

_____

    Why at this particular level? _____

_____

3. A 30 year old woman has a dominant sympathetic system. If you were her nurse, what problems might you expect to encounter and what type of environment should be maintained? _____

_____

_____

4. Why is a depressed skull fracture at the base of the brain often more dangerous than one in the frontal region? _____

_____

5. Briefly define the following.

   a. Lumbar sympathectomy: _____

_____

   b. Hyperhidrosis: _____

_____

   c. Tic douloureux: _____

6. A young boy has been admitted to a children's hospital for treatment of hydrocephalus. The doctor plans to do a ventriculoperitoneal shunt with polyethylene tubing.

   a. Define hydrocephalus: _____

_____

_____

_____

   b. Briefly, what does the doctor hope to do for his young patient?_____

_____

_____

_____

_____

7. A 55 year old man has a subdural hematoma which is exerting pressure on the area immediately anterior to the right central fissure (Rolando).

   a. Define subdural hematoma: _____

_____

_____

   b. What general symptoms would the lesion produce? _____

_____

_____

   c. Which side of the body would be involved? _____

_____

_____

Chapter 9

SPECIAL SENSES

Closely associated with the nervous system are certain receptor organs. Man's awareness of the world is limited to only those forms of energy, physical or chemical, to which his receptors are designed to respond. The sequence from stimulus to receptor to sensory nerve to the central nervous system is the physical basis of sensation. In the higher centers of the brain such impulses are interpreted as sensation.

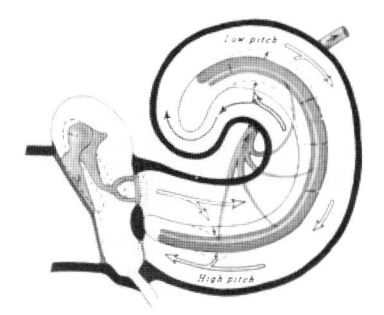

ANATOMY OF THE EYE

EXPERIMENT A: The Eye

PHYSIOLOGY OF THE EYE

EXPERIMENT B: Functions of the Eye
EXPERIMENT C: Optic Chiasm (optional)

ANATOMY OF THE EAR

EXPERIMENT D: The Ear

PHYSIOLOGY OF THE EAR

EXPERIMENT E: Functions of the Ear

PHYSIOLOGY OF OTHER SPECIAL SENSES

EXPERIMENT F: Taste
EXPERIMENT G: Smell
EXPERIMENT H: Pain, Touch, Heat, and Cold Receptors
         (optional)
PRACTICAL EXERCISES

ANATOMY OF THE EYE

EXPERIMENT A: The Eye

Materials:
    J & F, Ch. 9; appropriate chapters in Greisheimer, Kimber et al., Anthony, Reith et al., King & Showers, Chaffee & Greisheimer, Guyton.
Materials:
    1. Fresh animal eye (1)
    2. Model of the eye with removable parts
    3. Dissecting instruments and tray
  Objective: To observe the general physiological and structural characteristics of the eye.
  Procedure:
    1. Using the references indicated above, examine the external structure of the eye to identify the following:

Conjunctiva	Optic nerve
Extrinsic muscles	Fat pads

2. Cut muscles and fat away from the eye; identify the sclera (note color).

3. With a fine pair of sharp scissors make a cut from the optic nerve to the center of the cornea. Make similar incisions at a 90° angle to the first so that when the tissue is removed, about one-quarter of the covering of the eyeball will be lifted off; locate and observe the following:

Choroid coat	Retina
Ciliary processes	Anterior chamber
Iris	Posterior chamber
Pupil	Aqueous humor

(Save lens and vitreous humor for Experiment B)

4. Using the references indicated above, examine the model of eye and identify the following. Label Figures 57 to 60 with these terms.

Anterior chamber	Ciliary ligaments
Posterior chamber	Optic nerve
Choroid coat	Optic disc
Ciliary processes	Retina
Ciliary muscles	Sclera
Cornea	Suspensory ligament
Iris	Macula lutea
Lens	Pupil
Central artery and	Conjunctiva
vein of retina	Vitreous body
Lateral and medial	Superior and inferior rectus
rectus muscle	muscle
	Inferior oblique m.
	Superior oblique m.

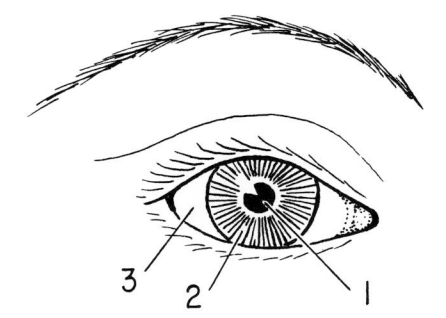

Figure 57. External structures of the eye.

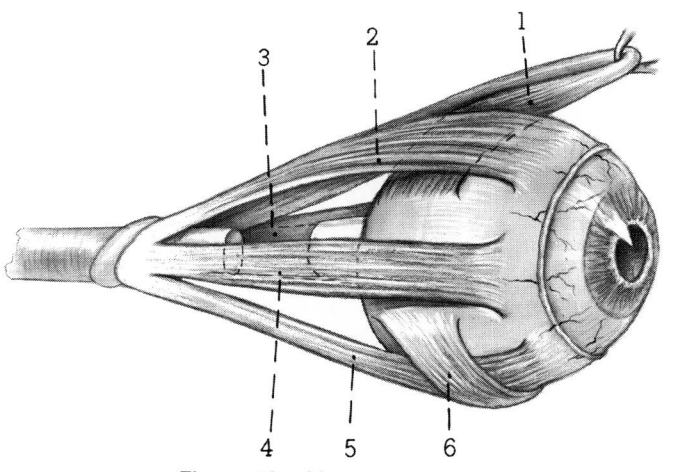

Figure 58. Muscles of the eye.

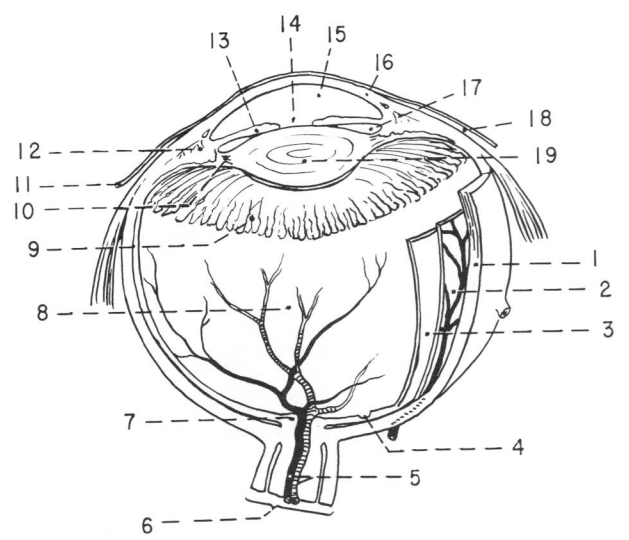

Figure 59. Midsagittal section of the eye.

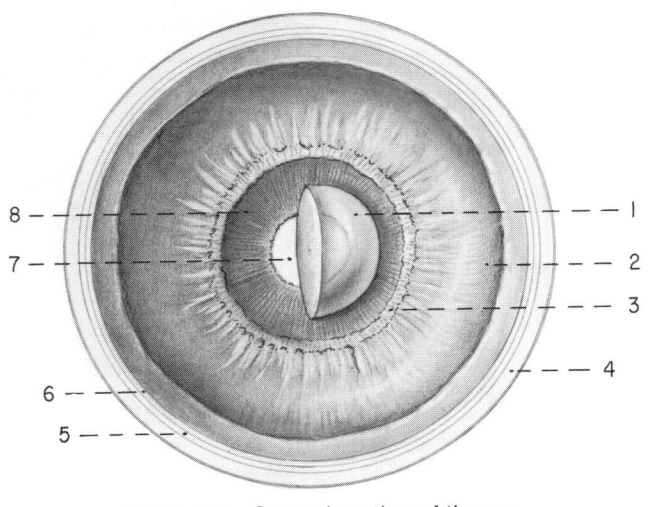

Figure 60. Coronal section of the eye.

PHYSIOLOGY OF THE EYE

EXPERIMENT B: Functions of the Eye

References:
 J & F, Ch. 9; appropriate chapters in Greisheimer, Guyton, Chaffee & Greisheimer.

Materials:
 1. Fresh lens and vitreous humor from eye
 2. Snellen visual acuity chart
 3. Color blind charts (if available)

Objective: To demonstrate blind spot, function of lens, pupillary response, visual acuity, and color blindness.

Procedure:

 1. Remove lens from the eye. Write two words on a piece of white paper and place the lens on one word and the vitreous humor over the other.

 a. Describe the difference in the appearance of the two words:

 _____

 _____

 b. What does this suggest to you about the physics of incoming light rays? _____

 _____

 2. Hold this page about 20 inches from the face with the cross in Figure 61 directly in front of the right eye. You should be able to see the cross and the circle when you close the left eye. Now, keeping the left eye closed, slowly bring the page closer to the face while fixing the right eye on the cross. At a certain distance the circle will disappear from your field of vision because its image falls upon the blind spot. Define the blind spot: _____

 _____

 3. Allow a strong light from a window or lamp to fall on your eyes and then look at a dark surface away from the light while your partner observes the pupils of your eyes. Next place your hand over one eye for a minute and upon removing it have the reaction of the pupil observed. Now cover one eye and allow your partner to observe the pupil of the other. Describe what happens to the pupils in these three situations: _____

 _____

 _____

$+$ ●

Figure 61. Demonstration of the blind spot.

4. Look through a pinhole in a sheet of paper at a well-illuminated surface such as that of a reading lamp. Close the other eye and note the size of the illuminated field. Upon opening the closed eye, note that the field becomes reduced in size. The changes in the size of the field are the result of the alternate constriction and dilatation of the pupil brought about by movement of the iris.

5. Feel the two eyes through the closed lids as voluntary eye movements are made. Open one eye and focus it on various objects around the room while feeling the other through the closed lid.

a. What do you observe? _____

_____

_____

b. Explain: _____

_____

6. Glance at the sun for a split second and observe the afterimage that appears.

a. Explain the result in terms of the bleaching effect of eye pigments.

_____

_____

7. Stand 20 feet away from a Snellen visual acuity chart placed at eye level. Measure your visual acuity without glasses and with glasses (if glasses are worn customarily). Results: _____

_____

_____

8. Observe color blind charts if available.

a. Are you deficient in color vision? If so, in what way? _____

_____

EXPERIMENT C: Optic Chiasm (optional)

References:

J & F, Ch. 9; appropriate chapters in Greisheimer, King & Showers, Chaffee & Greisheimer.

Procedure:

Study the references concerning nervous pathways for vision; then label Figure 62 of the optic chiasm with the following terms:

Optic nerve   Lateral ventricle
Optic chiasm   Geniculocalcarine tract
Lateral geniculate body

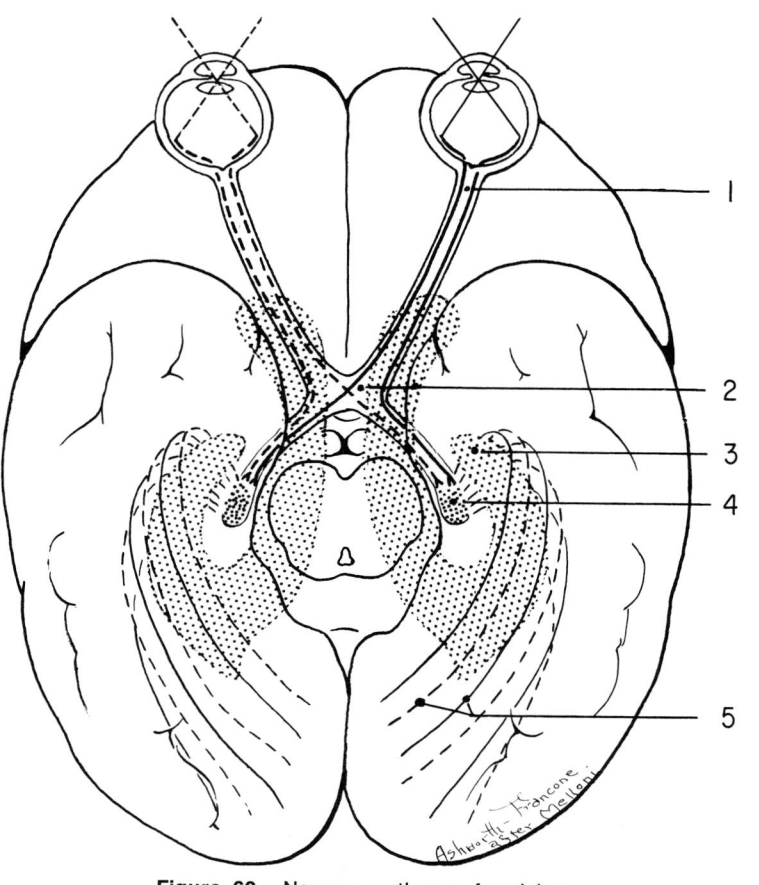

Figure 62.   Nervous pathways for vision.

ANATOMY OF THE EAR

EXPERIMENT D: The Ear

References:

J & F, Ch. 9; appropriate chapters in Greisheimer, Kimber et al., Anthony, Reith et al., King & Showers, Chaffee & Greisheimer, Guyton.

Materials:

1. Model of ear with removable parts
2. Histologic sections of cochlea (when available)

Objective: To observe the general physiological and structural characteristics of the ear.

Procedure:

1. Examine the model using the references indicated above to identify the structures listed below:

External auditory meatus	Incus (anvil)
Stapes (stirrup)	Malleus (hammer)
Cochlea	Semicircular canals
Ampullae	Auditory tube (eustachian tube)
Cochlear nerve	Facial nerve
Petrous temporal bone	Mastoid air cells
Squamous temporal bone	

2. Label Figure 63 with these terms.

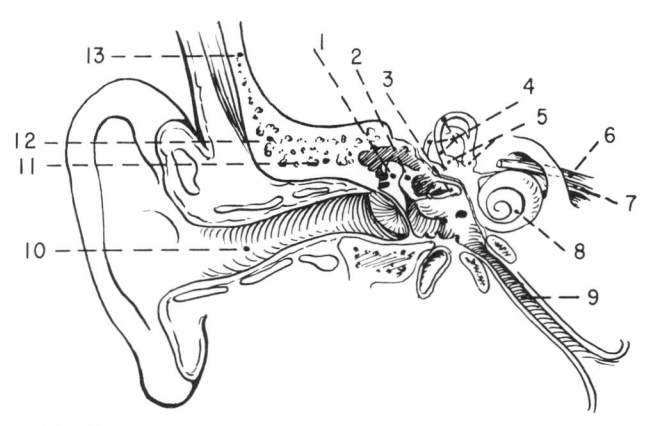

Figure 63.   Frontal section through the outer, middle, and internal ear.

3. Examine microscopic cross-sections of cochlea and identify the structures listed below:

Scala vestibuli   Vestibular membrane
Scala tympani   Tectorial membrane
Cochlear duct   Spiral ganglion
Basilar membrane

4. Label Figure 64 with these terms.

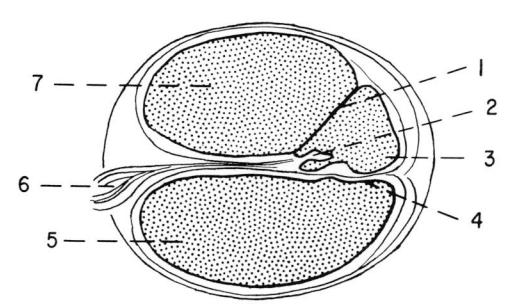

Figure 64. Cross section of the cochlea.

PHYSIOLOGY OF THE EAR

EXPERIMENT E: Functions of the Ear

References:

J & F, Ch. 9; appropriate chapters in Greisheimer, Guyton, Chaffee & Greisheimer.

Materials:

1. Tuning fork
2. Loud ticking watch
3. Frog or rat

Objective: To demonstrate the functions of the ears.

Procedure:

1. Place a frog or small rat on a table and observe the position of the head, body, and legs. Next put the animal on a rotating apparatus, turn it slowly, and observe the position of the body, head, and legs. Observe movements when rotation has stopped. Repeat, revolving the apparatus faster. Observe again.

Conclusions: _____

_____

_____

2. Stand erect, your feet close together and eyes closed. Observe for swaying and loss of balance, characteristic in disease of posterior white columns. This is the Romberg test used in neurological examinations.

   a. Results? _____

   _____

   b. Define kinesthesia: _____

   _____

3. Standing on one foot, hold your other foot and leg well off the floor; rotate your body several times on one heel with eyes closed. Observe movement of eyes. Normally the eyes respond to stimulation of the semicircular canals with a rhythmic jerking movement called nystagmus.

   a. Results? _____

   _____

   b. Define nystagmus: _____

   _____

4. Hold the handle of a vibrating tuning fork between your teeth. Where does the sound seem to originate? _____ Cover one ear. Does the source of the sound seem to be located as before? _____ Repeat, covering both ears. Any difference? _____ Explain your observations: _____

_____

_____

5. Rest the handle of a vibrating tuning fork upon the top of your head; when the sound is no longer audible remove it. After an interval of 5 seconds return the vibrating fork to the original position on the head. Is the sound heard

again after the period of rest? _____ Repeat the test with the tuning fork held at the side of the ear at a uniform distance from the head. Explain your observations: _____

_____

_____

_____

6. Test the ability of a blindfolded subject to locate a sound source (loud ticking watch, etc.) behind, above, in front of, and on both sides of him. Results:

_____

_____

7. Referring to procedure 4, explain why a person always exclaims upon hearing his voice coming from a tape recorder, "That does not sound like my voice!": _____

_____

_____

PHYSIOLOGY OF OTHER SPECIAL SENSES

EXPERIMENT F: Taste

References:

J & F, Ch. 9; appropriate chapters in Greisheimer, Anthony, King & Showers, Chaffee & Greisheimer, Guyton.

Materials:

1. Phenylthiocarbamide crystals
2. Q-tips
3. 3% sugar solution
4. 1% H_2SO_4 or citric acid solution
5. Quinine solution or epsom salt solution
6. 1% NaCl solution

Objective: To observe the distribution of taste buds.

Procedure:

1. Brush the following solution on the tip, sides, and back of your tongue. Rinse mouth with water after each solution is placed on your tongue. On Figure 65 sketch the areas most sensitive to each of the four substances.

Sweet (3% sugar solution)

Sour (1% H_2SO_4 or citric acid solution)

Bitter (quinine solution or epsom salt solution)

Salt (1% NaCl solution)

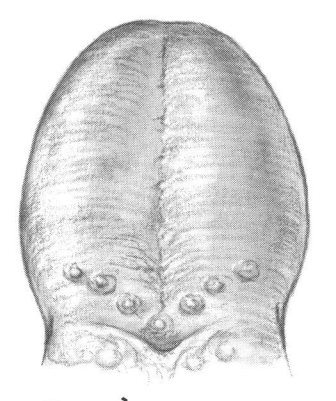

Figure 65.   The tongue.

2. Using the references indicated above, label Figure 66 as to distribution of taste papillae. Use the following terms:

      Epiglottis   Fungiform papilla
      Tonsil   Filiform papilla
      Circumvallate papilla

3. Place a few crystals of phenylthiocarbamide on your tongue. Approximately 70 per cent of a group will taste this substance; the other 30 per cent will not. What taste sensation did you experience? _____

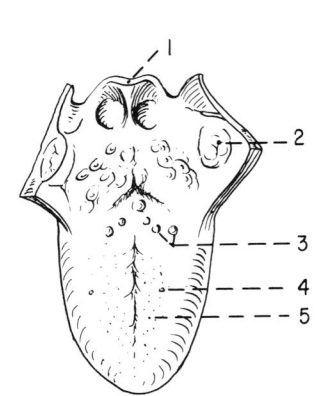

Figure 66. Dorsal view of the tongue.

EXPERIMENT G: Smell

References:

J & F, Ch. 9; appropriate chapters in Greisheimer, Kimber et al., Anthony, Guyton, Reith et al., King & Showers, Chaffee & Greisheimer.

Materials:

1. Small opened bottle of perfume
2. Small diameter rubber tubing
3. Tincture of iodine or oil of cloves
4. Small pieces of apple and raw potato
5. Funnel

Objective: To observe characteristics of smell.

Procedure:

1. Connect a piece of rubber tubing of small diameter to the tip of a glass funnel and place the funnel over a small opened bottle of perfume resting on a table. Insert the end of the tubi. .g into the lower posterior part of one nasal cavity and close the other nostril. Inhale through the nose and try to detect the odor. Repeat with the end of the tubing placed in the upper anterior part of the nasal cavity.

    a. What region gives the most distinct olfactory sensation? _____

    _____

    b. Where is the olfactory area located? _____

    _____

2. Close one nostril and with the other smell tincture of iodine or oil of cloves in a bottle held close to the nose. Expire through mouth and find the time interval necessary for olfactory exhaustion to be produced. Determine the time necessary for recovery. Repeat the test several times and obtain the average values.

    a. For fatigue: _____

    b. For recovery: _____

3. Fatigue the olfactory mechanism with tincture of iodine or oil of cloves and then breathe the volatile material from oil of peppermint or perfume.

    a. Is it possible to smell the second substances? _____

    b. Explain the results: _____

    _____

    _____

4. Sit with your eyes closed while your partner places small pieces of apple and raw potato on your tongue with forceps without telling you in advance which is to be used. Hold the nostrils closed while the tests are being made and try to identify the material placed on the tongue by taste alone. Does the flavor of food depend in part upon the sense of smell? _____

EXPERIMENT H: Pain, Touch, Heat and Cold Receptors (optional)

References:
> Appropriate chapters in Greisheimer, Kimber et al., Guyton, Chaffee & Greisheimer.

Materials:
> 1. Cotton
> 2. Needle
> 3. Metal probe
> 4. Bristle

Objective: To determine the distribution of pain, touch, heat and cold receptors.

Procedure:

1. On the inner surface of the wrist, near the palm, mark off a square 1.0 cm. on each side. In your notebook make a similar area. Rest your hand on the table. Close your eyes and have your partner explore the area marked off with the tip of a bristle that is pressed against the skin just enough to cause it to bend each time. The pressure should be applied in the same manner each time. Indicate when the sensation of touch is experienced and have your partner record on the paper with the square the corresponding points at which the sensations are felt.

Are the touch receptors uniformly distributed in the area investigated? _____

2. Mark off on the inner surface of the wrist a square, each side of which is 1.0 cm. long. Draw a similar area in your notebook. Apply a piece of absorbent cotton soaked with water to the area on the wrist for about 5 minutes to soften the skin. Use water as needed during the experiment. Place the point of a needle to the surface of the skin and press enough to produce a sensation of pain. Explore the area in a systematic manner, recording on the paper the locations of the points that give pain sensation when stimulated. Distinguish between sensations of touch and pain.

Are the areas for touch and pain identical? _____

3. On the back of the wrist mark off a square, each side of which is 2.0 cm. in length; place a metal probe or pointed rod in cold water for a minute, dry it quickly and, with the dull point, explore the area in the square for the existence of cold spots. Keep the probe cool and with ink mark the position of each spot found.

Immerse the probe or rod in hot water so that it will give a sensation of warmth when removed and applied to the skin, but avoid having it too hot. Proceeding as before, locate the position of the warm spots in the same area. Mark these spots with ink of a different color.

Which of these two types of sensations is more numerous within the area?

_____

4. Do cutaneous sensations differ in different parts of the body? _____

Explain: _____

_____

5. Located in the skin are specific receptors sensitive to the 4 basic sensations of pain, touch, temperature and pressure. Upon stimulation of a receptor, a nerve impulse is sent to the cerebral cortex of the brain where the impulse is interpreted. The brain must interpret between degrees of stimulation and between combinations of stimulations, the latter resulting in sensations such as burning, tickling or itching.

PRACTICAL EXERCISES

ANATOMY AND PHYSIOLOGY QUESTIONS

1. Name the extrinsic eye muscles: _____

_____

_____

_____

2. Which cranial nerve (number) is the optic nerve? _____

_____

3. Name the photosensitive cells of the retina: _____

_____

4. Name the region of the eyeball in which only cone cells are found:

_____

5. What causes binocular vision? _____

_____

_____

6. Explain the function of the auditory (eustachian) tube: _____

_____

_____

7. Which part of the ear contains receptors for the cochlear nerve (branch of the auditory nerve for hearing)? _____

_____

What name is given to these receptors? _____

8. Which part of the ear contains receptors for the vestibular branch of the auditory nerve? _____

_____

9. Describe the function of the vestibular nerve: _____

_____

_____

10. Name the auditory ossicles, giving two names for each: _____

_____

_____

CLINICAL QUESTIONS

1. Briefly define the following:

   a. Otosclerosis: _____

   _____

   b. Tinnitus: _____

   _____

     c. Cerumen: _____

_____

     d. Conjunctivitis: _____

_____

_____

     e. Astigmatism: _____

_____

     f. Myopia: _____

_____

     g. Glaucoma: _____

_____

2. Why would a person who has a lens removed be very sensitive to light?

_____

_____

3. Why is there a sensation of pressure in our ears when we experience a sudden change in altitude? _____

_____

_____

_____

4. Why may otitis media follow a severe cold or sore throat? _____

_____

_____

_____

5. What does an ophthalmoscopic examination reveal to a doctor? _____

_____

_____

_____

Chapter 10

THE CIRCULATORY SYSTEM

The circulatory system is a circuit providing a route for blood to flow from the periphery to the heart, then to the lungs, back to the heart, and to the periphery again. It is a means by which nutrition, oxygen, and electrolytes are taken to needed areas and, at the same time, a means by which metabolic wastes are carried away from tissues.

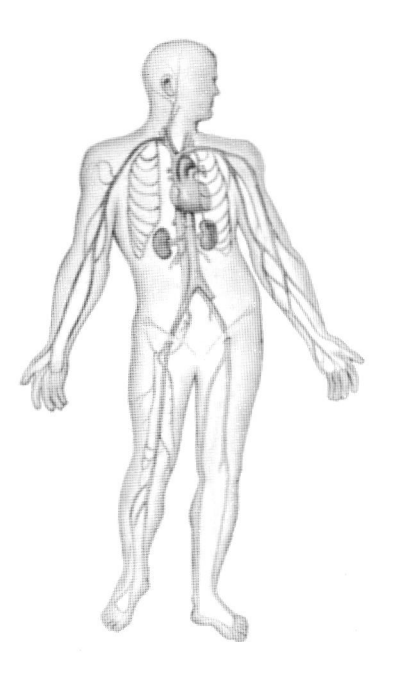

BLOOD

EXPERIMENT A: Preparation of Stained Blood Slide
EXPERIMENT B: Blood Tests
EXPERIMENT C: Determination of ABO Blood Grouping
              and Rh Factor
EXPERIMENT D: Red and White Blood Cell Counting
              (optional)

ANATOMY OF THE CIRCULATORY SYSTEM

EXPERIMENT E: Dissection of Animal Heart
EXPERIMENT F: Structure of Blood Vessels
EXPERIMENT G: Major Arteries of the Body
EXPERIMENT H: Major Veins of the Body

PHYSIOLOGY OF THE CIRCULATORY SYSTEM

EXPERIMENT I: Pulse Rate and Blood Pressure
EXPERIMENT J: Heart Sounds
EXPERIMENT K: Hyperemia
PRACTICAL EXERCISES

BLOOD

EXPERIMENT A: Preparation of Stained Blood Slide

References:
J & F, Ch. 10; Appropriate chapters in Greisheimer, Kimber et al., Anthony, Guyton, Reith et al., King & Showers, Dienhart, Chaffee & Greisheimer.

Materials:
1. Cotton
2. 70% alcohol
3. Blood lancets
4. Glass slides
5. Cover slips
6. Wright's stain (see appendix)
7. Wright's buffer (see appendix)
8. Leukemia blood smear slide
9. Distilled water

Objective: To observe the types of blood cells.

Procedure:

1. Wash hands with soap and water. Sponge the fingertip with 70% alcohol. Air dry.

2. Puncture fingertip with a sterile lancet or needle.

3. Place a drop of blood about 1 inch from the end of the slide and smear with the end of another slide. *(Instructor will demonstrate.)* Let the smear dry.

4. Cover with Wright's stain and allow to stand for 2 minutes. The stain should cover the slide but not overflow.

5. Cover with an equal amount of Wright's buffer and let stand for 4 minutes. *NOTE:* Distilled water may be used in place of Wright's buffer if the stain is not too alkaline.

6. Rinse the slide with distilled water until it appears light blue and translucent.

7. Allow to dry in the air.

8. Examine the smear under oil immersion. Using the references, identify and make colored sketches of:

    a. Leukocytes
        Neutrophil
        Lymphocyte
        Eosinophil (if possible)
        Monocyte
        Basophil (if possible)
    b. Erythrocytes

9. Using a reference, make a differential blood count. What is the normal differential concentration of leukocytes?

        Neutrophils _____%

        Lymphocytes _____%

        Eosinophils _____%

        Monocytes _____%

        Basophils _____%

10. Examine a blood smear of a patient with leukemia. How does this differ from normal blood? _____

_____

_____

_____

EXPERIMENT B: Blood Tests

References:
> J & F, Ch. 10; appropriate chapters in Greisheimer, Kimber et al., Anthony, Guyton, Reith et al., King & Showers, Dienhart, Chaffee & Greisheimer.

Materials:
1. 70% alcohol
2. Cotton
3. Blood lancets
4. Stop watch
5. Test tube of blood (for demonstration)
6. Fresh, whole blood (for demonstration)
7. Wire beater
8. Benzidine reagent
9. Filter paper
10. Frog
11. Ether

Objective: To observe characteristics of blood.

Procedure:
1. Duke method for determining bleeding time.
   a. Cleanse ear lobe with 70% alcohol and let dry.
   b. Puncture lobe with sterile lancet.
   c. Record time interval from first freely falling drop until bleeding stops (normal, 1 to 3 minutes). Result: _____

   _____

2. Observe a test tube containing a sample of blood that was permitted to stand undisturbed (demonstration).

   a. Has the blood clotted? _____

   b. What is the liquid at top of tube? _____

   _____

   c. In what way does this liquid differ from blood plasma? _____

   _____

   _____

3. Distinguish between "bleeding time" and "clotting time." _____

_____

_____

4. Obtain some fresh, whole blood that has been whipped with a wire beater (demonstration).

   a. What are the long strands of fibers that you observe? _____

   _____

5. Benzidine test (test for hemoglobin): Add a drop of benzidine reagent to a piece of filter paper. Next add a drop of blood to the filter paper. A dark

blue-green color is a positive test for hemoglobin. What clinical use could be made of this test? _____

_____

_____

_____

     6. Hematocrit: Add a sample of blood to a hematocrit tube; next add an anticoagulant (see appendix) and centrifuge (Figure 67).

        a. What per cent of the blood is formed elements? _____

        b. What per cent of the blood is plasma? _____

     7. Anesthetize a frog (follow procedure in Chapter 1, Experiment C) and examine the web of the frog's foot mounted under the low or medium power of a microscope. Distinguish among capillaries, arterioles, and venules: _____

_____

_____

_____

_____

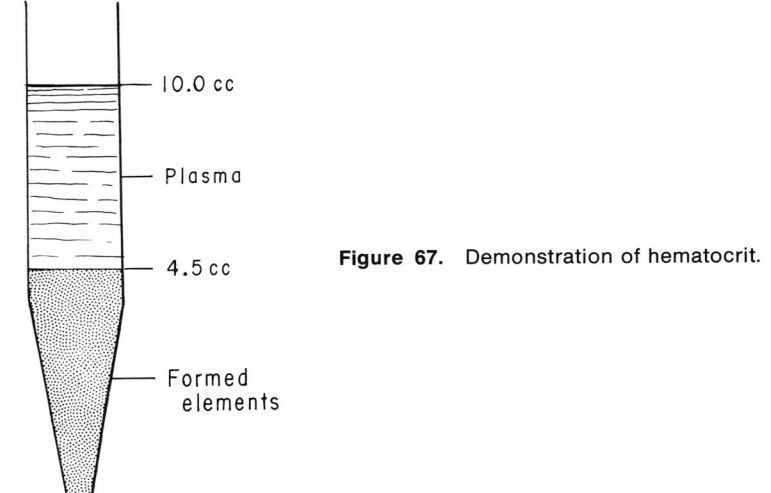

Figure 67. Demonstration of hematocrit.

EXPERIMENT C: Determination of ABO Blood Grouping and Rh Factor

References:

J & F, Ch. 10; appropriate chapters in Greisheimer, Kimber et al., Anthony, Guyton, Reith et al., King & Showers, Dienhart, Chaffee & Greisheimer.

Materials:

1. 70% alcohol
2. Cotton
3. Blood lancets
4. Glass slides
5. Anti-A serum
6. Anti-B serum
7. Rh serum (anti-D type)
8. Toothpicks

Objective: Determination of ABO Grouping and Rh factor

Procedure:

1. a. Wash hands with soap and water. Sponge fingertip with 70% alcohol. Puncture tip with a sterile lancet or needle.
   b. On two slides labeled A and B place a drop of your blood.
   c. Add a drop of anti-A serum (group B) to the blood drop on slide A. To slide B add a drop of anti-B serum (group A).
   d. Mix the serum and cells by slightly tilting and gently rotating the slide. With the naked eye examine for agglutination (clumping). Agglutination may take several minutes.
      (1) If the cells being tested belong to group AB, there will be agglutination on both slides A and B.
      (2) If the cells are of group A, there will be agglutination only on slide A.
      (3) If the cells are of group B, there will be agglutination only on slide B.
      (4) If the cells are of group 0, neither slide A nor B will show agglutination.

2. Give the reasons for the above results: _____

_____

_____

_____

3. Add a drop of Rh serum (anti-D type) to a slide.
   a. Add a small drop of your blood to the Rh serum.
   b. Stir and spread out the drops with a toothpick.
   c. Heat slightly by bringing the slide close to a light bulb.
   d. Rh positive blood will clump at the end of 2 min.; Rh negative blood will not clump.

EXPERIMENT D: Red and White Blood Cell Counting (Excellent detailed descriptions of technique and methods will be found in the following references.)

References:

Bauer, J. D., Toro, G., and Ackerman, P. G.: Bray's Clinical Laboratory Methods. The C. V. Mosby Co., St. Louis, 1962.

Dacie, J. V., and Lewis, S. M.: Practical Hematology. Grune & Stratton, Inc., New York, 1963.

Wintrobe, M. M.: Clinical Hematology. Lea and Febiger, Philadelphia, 1967.

ANATOMY OF THE CIRCULATORY SYSTEM

EXPERIMENT E: Dissection of Animal Heart

References:

J & F, Ch. 10; appropriate chapters in Greisheimer, Kimber et al., Anthony, Reith et al., King & Showers, Chaffee & Greisheimer, appropriate animal dissection guide (see appendix).

Materials:

1. Preserved beef, sheep, or other animal heart
2. Heart models
3. Dissecting instruments and tray

Objective: To observe the gross characteristics of the heart.

Procedure:

1. Preliminary gross examination (use references above).
   a. Observe the pericardium surrounding the heart.

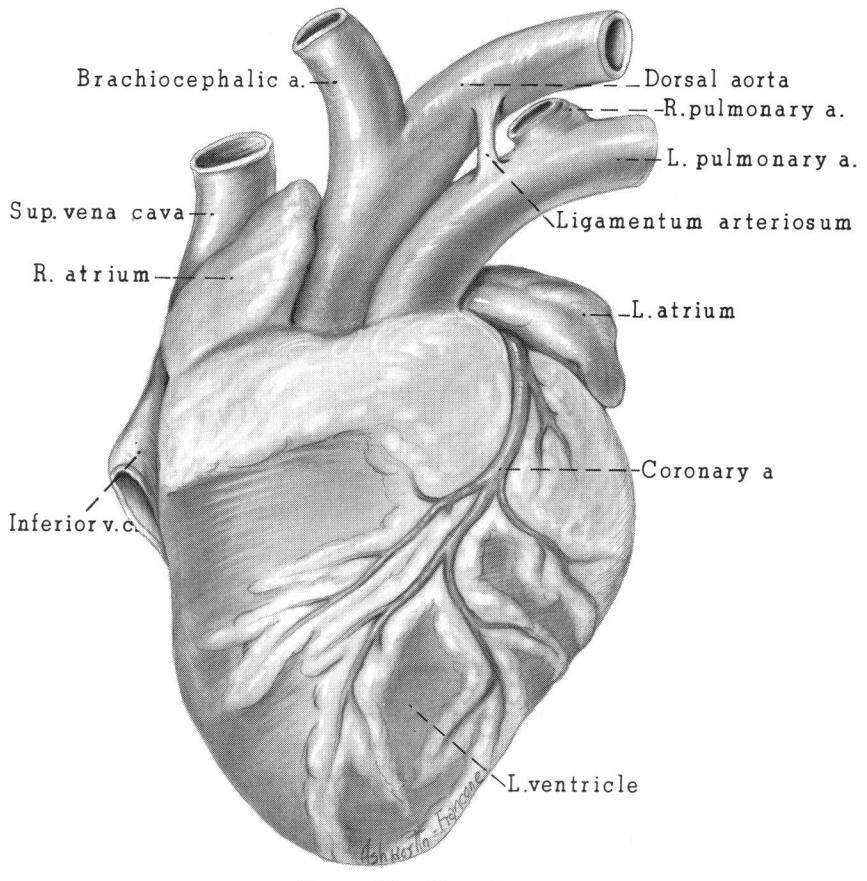

Figure 68. Sheep heart.

b. Slit the pericardium and distinguish between the visceral and parietal layers.

c. Note the fat around the coronary arteries and veins on the surface of the heart.

d. Examine the two auricular appendages which are extensions of the upper chambers (atria) of the heart.

e. Feel the walls of the lower part of the heart. Does one side feel thicker than the other?

The thicker side is the _____ ventricle.

The thinner side is the _____ ventricle.

2. Right heart

a. Note the two large veins entering the right atrium. What are they called? _____ and _____

b. With scissors cut down the right side of the vessels, atrium, and right ventricle. Discard any clotted blood which may be present.

c. Note how many leaves there are to the valve between the right atrium and the right ventricle _____.

Name this valve: _____

d. The lining of the heart is called the: _____

e. Note the muscular structures giving rise to the tendinous strings attached to the valve leaflets.

The muscles are called _____ muscles.

The strings are called _____

Their function is _____

3. Left heart

a. The vessels entering the left atrium are called _____

b. Cut down the left side of a pulmonary vein through the atrium and continue down through the ventricle to the apex; then cut back up through the aorta. After doing this, you should have a U-shaped incision which will allow examination of the interior.

c. How many cusps does the valve between the left atrium and left ventricle have? _____ What is this valve called? _____

d. How many valve flaps are there on the valve between the left ventricle and the aorta? _____ Name this valve:

_____

e. Name the two small openings just above the valve flaps:

_____. These vessels carry blood to:

_____

4. Find on the animal heart and heart models the following terms. Label Figure 69, placing the correct term next to each letter indicating a chamber and each number indicating a structure:

Right ventricle   Right atrium
Left ventricle   Left atrium
Mitral valve   Interventricular septum

Chordae tendinae
Pulmonary artery
Superior and inferior
   venae cavae
Pulmonary veins

Tricuspid valve
Aorta
Pulmonary valve
Papillary muscle
Aortic valve

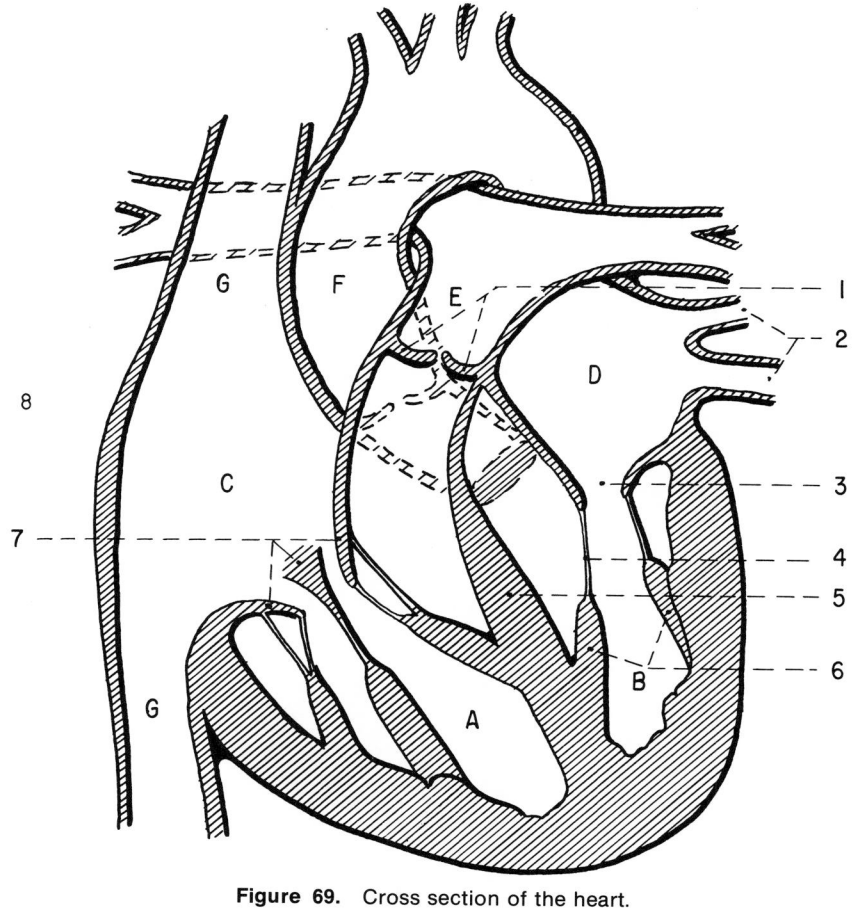

Figure 69. Cross section of the heart.

5. Find the following structures on the animal heart and heart models:

Aorta

Anterior descending branch
   (interventricular)

Left coronary artery

Posterior descending branch
   (interventricular)

Pulmonary artery

Coronary sinus

Anterior cardiac vein

Left atrial appendage

Right atrial appendage

Circumflex artery

Right coronary artery

Superior vena cava

Great cardiac vein

Small cardiac vein

Middle cardiac vein
   (posterior)

6. Label Figures 70 and 71 with the above terms.

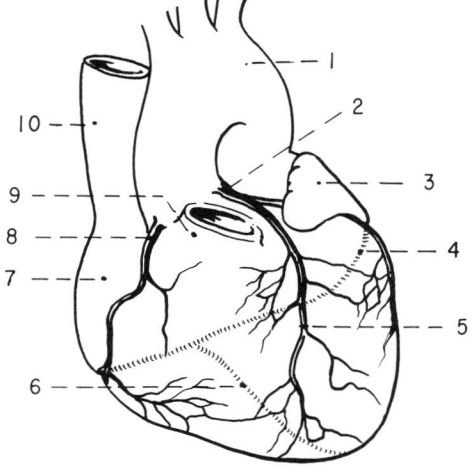

Figure 70. Coronary arteries.

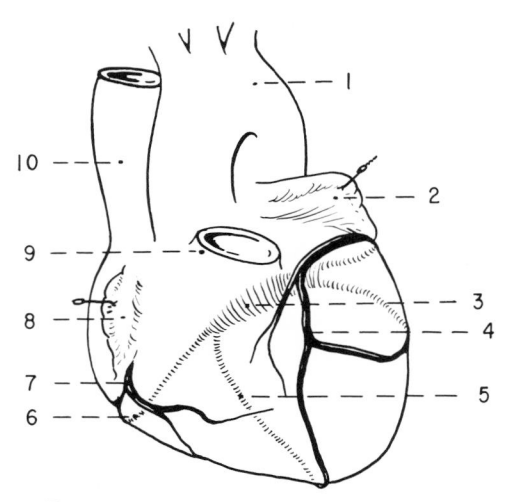

Figure 71. Venous drainage of the heart.

EXPERIMENT F: Structure of Blood Vessels

References:

J & F, Ch. 10; appropriate chapters in Greisheimer, Kimber et al., Anthony, Reith et al., King & Showers, Chaffee & Greisheimer, Ham & Leeson.

Materials:

1. Preserved animal heart
2. Histologic section of arteries, veins, capillaries (slide of umbilical cord)

Objective: To observe gross and microscopic characteristics of blood vessels.

Procedure:

1. On an animal heart, compare and contrast the aorta and vena cava.

Describe the most obvious difference: _____

_____

_____

2. Examine slides or illustrations showing the microscopic structure of arteries, veins (see Figure 72).

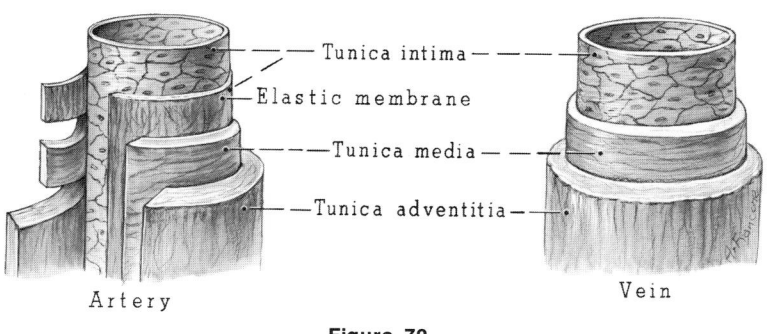

Artery   Vein

Figure 72.

Name the tissue layers that compose the walls of arteries: _____

_____

Of veins: _____

_____

     3. Is capillary blood flow pulsating, steady, or irregular? _____

_____

Why? _____

_____

     4. How does the diameter of red blood cells compare with that of the capillary lumen? _____

_____

     5. Arteries convey blood from the _____ to the

_____

     6. Arteries are composed of three tissue layers. Nourishment of tissue cells in these layers depends on networks of tiny blood vessels called _____

_____

     7. How do the elastic fibers and muscular coat of an artery function in the arrest of hemorrhage? _____

_____

_____

EXPERIMENT G: Major Arteries of the Body

References:

J & F, Ch. 10; appropriate animal dissection guide; appropriate chapters in Greisheimer, Kimber et al., Anthony, Reith et al., King & Showers, Chaffee & Greisheimer.

Materials:

Injected preserved animal

Objective: To observe the major arteries of the body.

Procedure:

1. Using the animal reference materials above, find as many arteries on the injected preserved animal as your instructor directs.

2. Label Figures 73 and 74 with the following terms:

Common carotid a.	Testicular (ovarian) a.
Subclavian a.	Superior mesenteric a.
Aorta	Brachial a.
Heart	Axillary a.
Celiac trunk a.	First rib
Renal a.	Brachiocephalic a.
Inferior mesenteric a.	Internal thoracic a.
Abdominal a.	Vertebral a.
Common iliac a.	Anterior communicating a.
Internal iliac (hypogastric) a.	Anterior cerebral a.
Femoral a.	Internal carotid a.
Profunda femoris a.	Middle cerebral a.
Dorsalis pedis a.	Posterior communicating a.
Anterior tibial a.	Posterior cerebral a.
Descending branch of	Basilar a.
lateral femoral	Deep palmar arch
circumflex a.	Radial a.
Superficial palmar arch	Ulnar a.

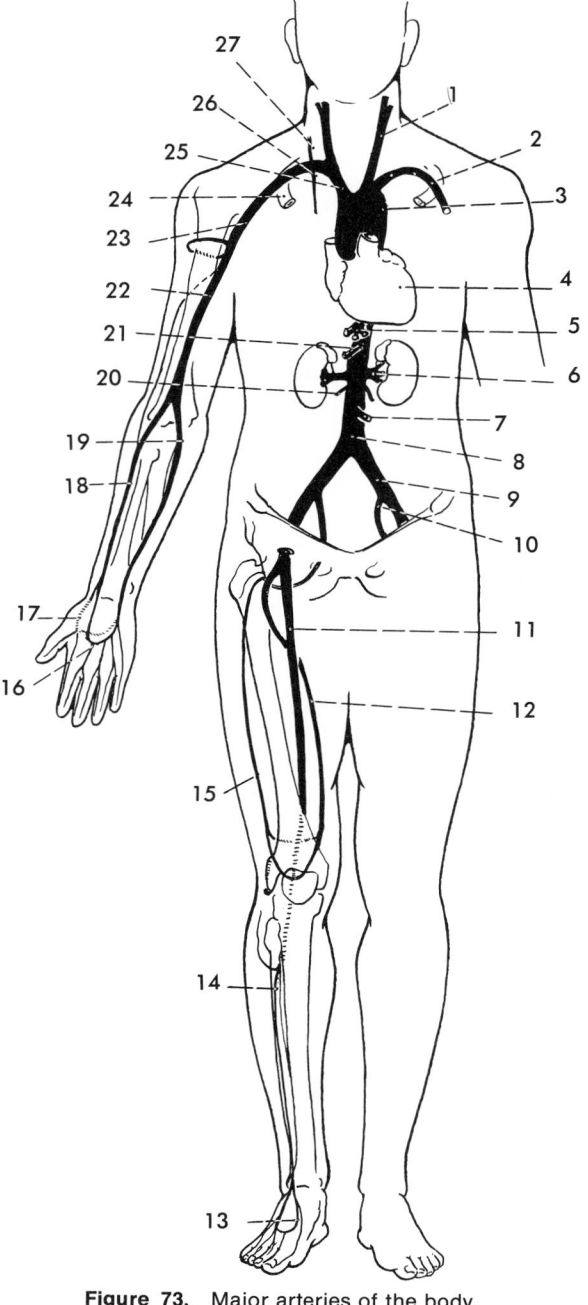

Figure 73. Major arteries of the body.

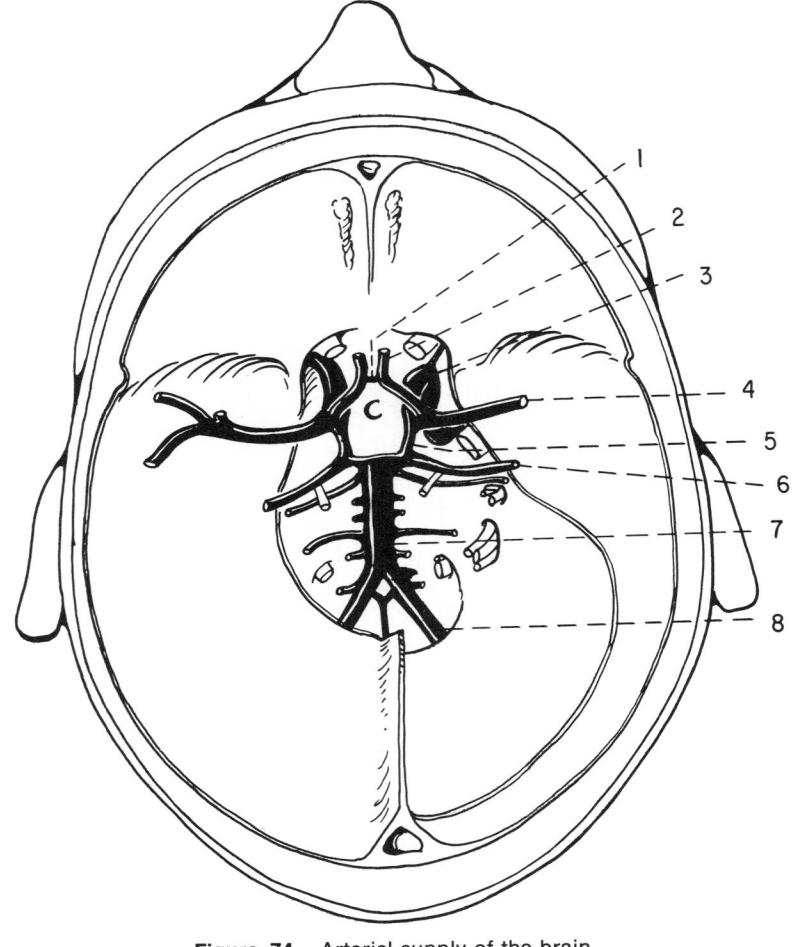

Figure 74.   Arterial supply of the brain.

EXPERIMENT H: Major Veins of the Body

References:

J & F, Ch. 10; appropriate animal dissection guide; appropriate chapters in Greisheimer, Kimber et al., Anthony, Reith et al., King & Showers, Chaffee & Greisheimer.

Materials:

Injected preserved animal

Objective: To observe the major veins of the body.

Procedure:

1. Using the reference materials listed above, find as many veins on the injected preserved animal as your instructor thinks are important.

2. Label Figures 75 and 76 with the following terms:

Internal jugular v.	Median cubital v.
External jugular v.	Inferior vena cava
First rib	Brachial v.
Superior vena cava	Axillary v.
Hepatic v.	Cephalic v.
Suprarenal v.	Brachiocephalic v.
Renal v.	Inferior sagittal sinus
Left testicular (ovarian) v.	Superficial temporal v.
Common iliac (hypo-	Superior ophthalmic v.
gastric) v.	Supra-orbital v.
External iliac v.	Cavernous sinus
Femoral v.	Angular v.
Great saphenous v.	Inferior ophthalmic v.
Dorsal venous arch	Pterygoid plexus
Anterior tibial v.	Deep facial v.
Popliteal v.	Anterior facial v.
Superficial palmar network	Superior thyroid v.
Basilic v.	Transverse sinus
Thyroid gland	Straight sinus
Inferior thyroid v.	Inferior petrosal sinus
Right brachiocephalic v.	Superior petrosal sinus
Right axillary v.	Superior sagittal sinus
Right subclavian v.	Vertebral v.
Deep cervical v.	Sigmoid sinus
Occipital plexus	Parietal emissary v.
Small saphenous v.	

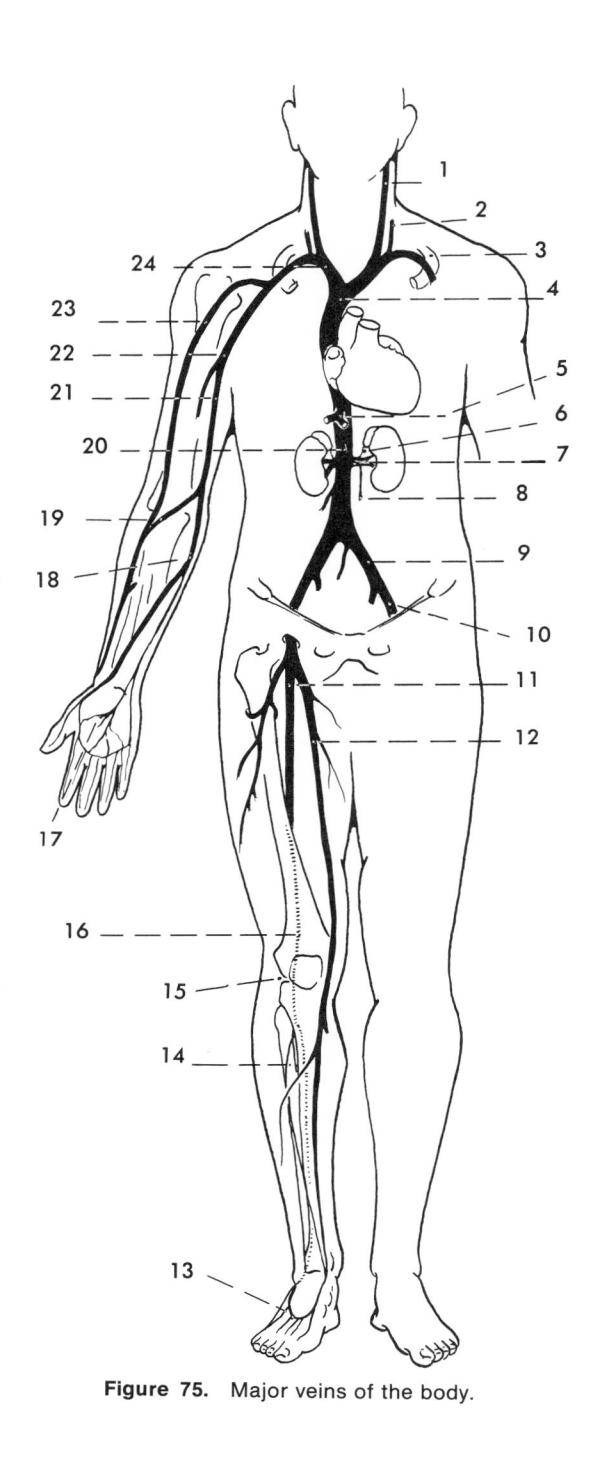

Figure 75. Major veins of the body.

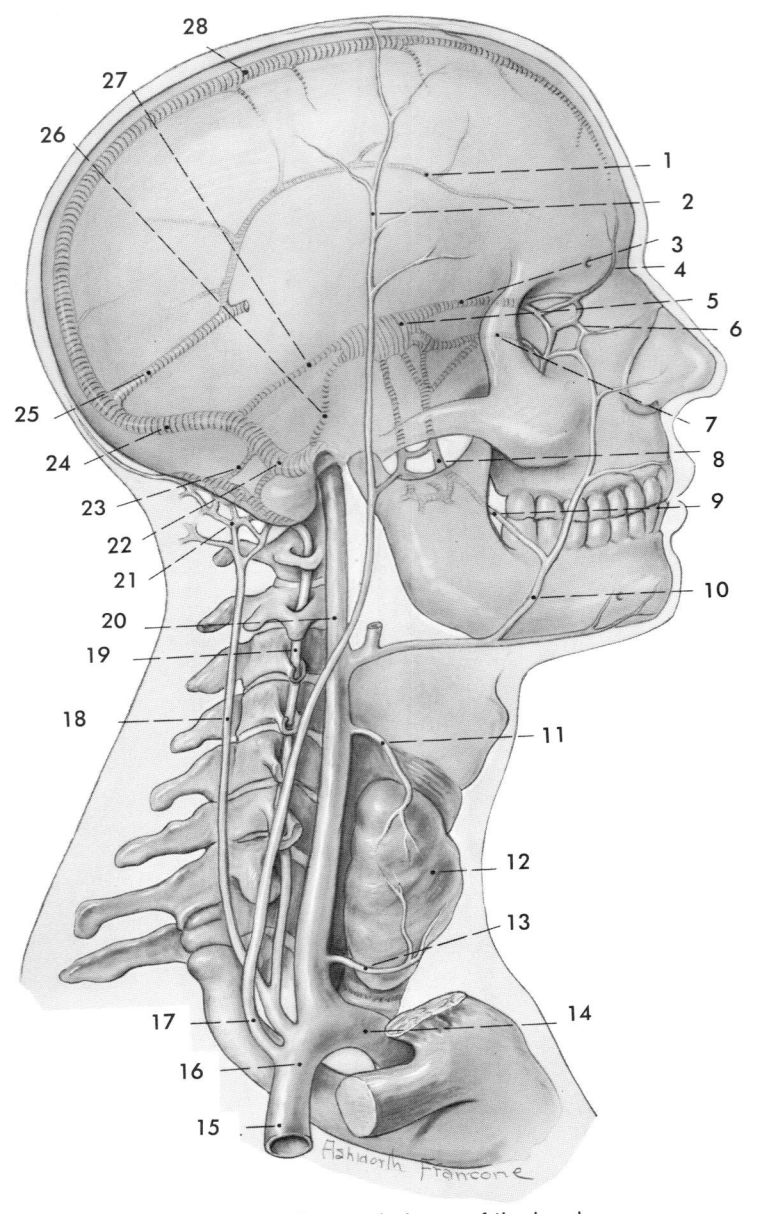

Figure 76. Venous drainage of the head.

PHYSIOLOGY OF THE CIRCULATORY SYSTEM

EXPERIMENT I: Pulse Rate and Blood Pressure

References:

J & F, Ch. 10; appropriate chapters in Greisheimer, Kimber et al., Anthony, Guyton, Reith et al., King & Showers, Dienhart, Chaffee & Greisheimer; *Recommendations for Human Blood Pressure Determination by Sphygmomanometer;* supplied by Local Heart Association.

Materials:

1. Blood pressure cuff
2. Amyl nitrite ampules

Objective: To show effects of exercise and amyl nitrite on pulse and blood pressure.

Procedure:

1. Effects of exercise
    a. Subject sitting quietly in a chair.

    Blood pressure: _____

    Pulse rate: _____

    b. Subject after exercising (e.g., running in place for 2 minutes)

    Blood pressure: _____

    Pulse rate: _____

    c. What are the effects of exercise on blood pressure and pulse rate?

    Discuss. _____

    _____

    _____

    _____

    _____

    _____

2. Inhalation of amyl nitrite
    a. Subject No. 2 sitting quietly in a chair.

    Blood pressure: _____

    Pulse rate: _____

    b. Crush amyl nitrite "pearl" (glass ampule) in a handkerchief and allow subject to take 2 or 3 inhalations.
    Note: Take blood pressure immediately!

    Blood pressure: _____

    Pulse rate: _____

    Appearance of skin: _____

    c. What is the action of this drug? _____

    _____

    _____

EXPERIMENT J: Heart Sounds

References:

J & F, Ch. 10; appropriate chapters in Greisheimer, Kimber et al., Guyton, Reith et al., King & Showers, Dienhart, Chaffee & Greisheimer.

Materials:

Stethoscope

Objective: To become familiar with the basic heart sounds and the use of the stethoscope.

Procedure:

1. Using the references listed above, place a stethoscope on the chest over the area of the cardiac apex. Correlating the timing of the sounds with the carotid pulse, try to deduce the relationship of each of the sounds to the period during which blood is ejected from the heart.

2. There are four areas on the chest where the sounds produced by four sets of valves may be differentially heard (Fig. 77).

   a. At the apex of the heart in the fifth intercostal space near the nipple — the mitral (bicuspid) area. (First sound — systole)
   b. In the second left intercostal space near the sternum — pulmonic area. (Second sound — diastole)
   c. In the second right intercostal space near the sternum — aortic area. (Second sound — diastole)
   d. At the bottom of the sternum near the xiphoid cartilage — tricuspid area. (First sound — systole)

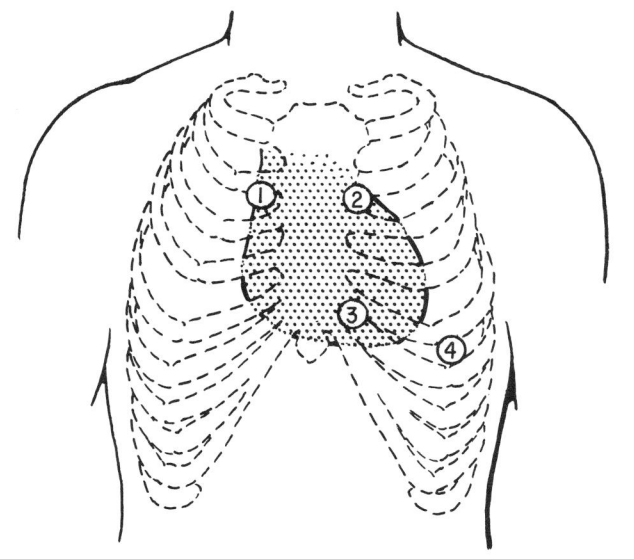

Figure 77. Location of heart sounds.

3. Try to note the differences in the sounds observed at these four positions. Be certain to understand the relationship of valve action to mechanical events and sound production.

4. Valvular abnormalities might be expected to be associated with abnormal sound production. Normal sounds are produced by mechanical impact and tension on valve leaflets. Turbulent flow through a narrowed orifice may produce sounds in the heart and great vessels. Sound is also produced when the valves do not close completely and blood gushes backward.

EXPERIMENT K: Hyperemia

References:
   Anthony, Ch. 9.
Materials:
   1. Beaker of hot water
   2. Rubber band
   3. Thermometer
Objective: To demonstrate hyperemia
Procedure:

1. Wind a rubber band above the second joint of your finger. Wait several minutes.

    a. Is there a change in size and color of the finger? _____

    _____

    Why? _____

    _____

2. Immerse the finger in hot water (45° C.) for a few minutes.
    a. Is there a difference in appearance of the finger size and color?

    _____

    _____

    Why? _____

    _____

    b. Are there sensations other than warmth present? _____

    _____

    Why? _____

    _____

3. What are the syptoms of hyperemia? _____

_____

4. Define hyperemia: _____

_____

PRACTICAL EXERCISES

ANATOMY AND PHYSIOLOGY QUESTIONS

    1. Name the different types of white blood cells: _____

_____

_____

_____

    2. What is a sphygmomanometer? _____

_____

_____

_____

    3. Trace the flow of blood from tissues to the heart and back to the tissues:

_____

_____

_____

_____

    4. Name the four heart valves: _____ , _____ ,

_____ , and _____ .

    5. Define "blood pressure": _____

_____

_____

_____

    6. What is the average range for blood pressure? _____

    7. List the major factors involved in the maintenance of arterial blood pressure: _____

_____

_____

    8. The "pulse" is caused by: _____

_____

_____

    9. List the three basic steps in the formation of a fibrin clot:

        a. _____

        b. _____

        c. _____

CLINICAL QUESTIONS

1. Why is it that when your knees are crossed in a particular way your lifted foot will jerk up and down in a rhythmic fashion? _____

_____

_____

_____

2. Briefly define the following:

a. Pericarditis: _____

_____

b. Syncope: _____

c. Angina pectoris: _____

_____

d. Anemia: _____

_____

e. Thrombophlebitis: _____

_____

3. What are the commonest causes of shock? _____

_____

_____

_____

4. What is meant by varicose veins? _____

_____

_____

What is the treatment for varicose veins? _____

_____

_____

5. Distinguish between a thrombus and an embolus: _____

_____

_____

Chapter 11

THE LYMPHATIC SYSTEM

The lymphatic system represents an accessory route by which fluids can flow from the interstitial spaces back to the blood. Most important of all, the lymphatics can carry proteins and even large particulate matter away from the tissue spaces, neither of which can be removed directly by the blood capillaries.

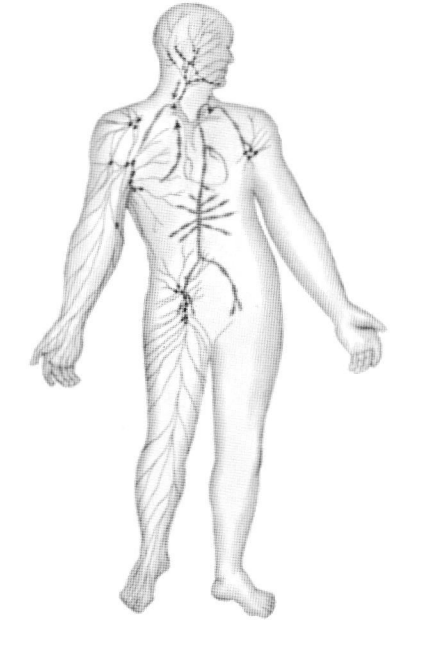

ANATOMY OF LYMPHATIC SYSTEM
EXPERIMENT A: Completion of Diagram of Lymphatic System
EXPERIMENT B: Histology of Lymph Nodes and Vessels
PRACTICAL EXERCISES

ANATOMY OF LYMPHATIC SYSTEM

EXPERIMENT A: Completion of Diagram of Lymphatic System (Fig. 78)

References:
    J & F, Ch. 11; appropriate chapters in Greisheimer, Kimber et al., Anthony, Guyton, Reith et al., King & Showers.
Objective: Location of lymph nodes and drainage areas.
Procedure:
    1. Using the references listed above, add small "x" marks to indicate areas where lymph nodes are most abundant (Figure 78).
    2. With colored pencils, lightly shade those portions of the body which are drained by the right lymphatic duct and the thoracic duct.

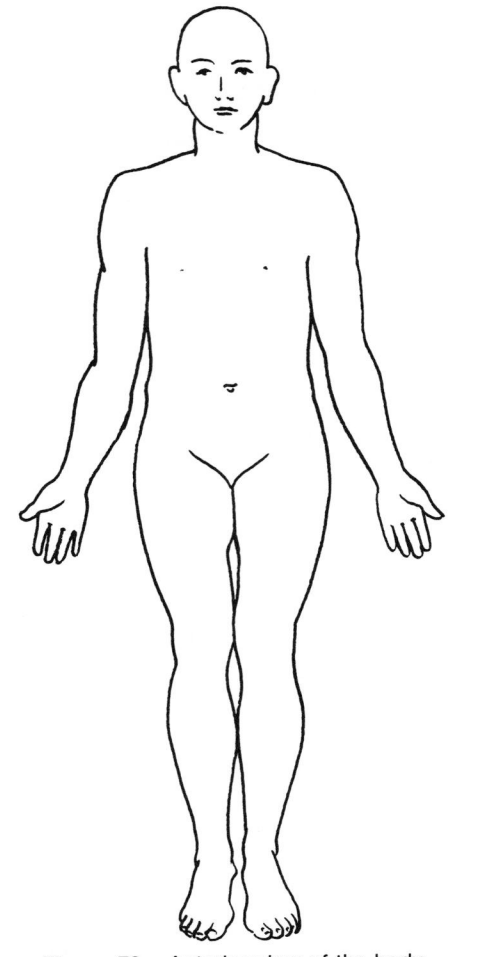

Figure 78.   Anterior view of the body.

EXPERIMENT B: Histology of Lymph Nodes and Vessels

References:
> J & F, Ch. 11; appropriate chapters in Greisheimer, Kimber et al., Anthony, Reith et al., King & Showers, Ham & Leeson.

Materials:
1. Microscope
2. Histologic sections of lymph nodes
3. Sections of skin

Objective: To visualize the microscopic structure of lymph nodes.

Procedure:

1. Using references above examine slides of lymph node tissue under a microscope, finding as many of the following structures as possible:

Medullary cord	Reticulo-endothelial cells
Primary cortical nodule	Reticulum
	Hilus
Trabecula	Efferent and afferent lymphatics
Capsule	Fat

2. Label Figure 79 with the above terms.

3. Examine sections of skin under highpower and see if you can locate lymphatic vessels in the dermis. They are near capillaries and contain no red blood cells.

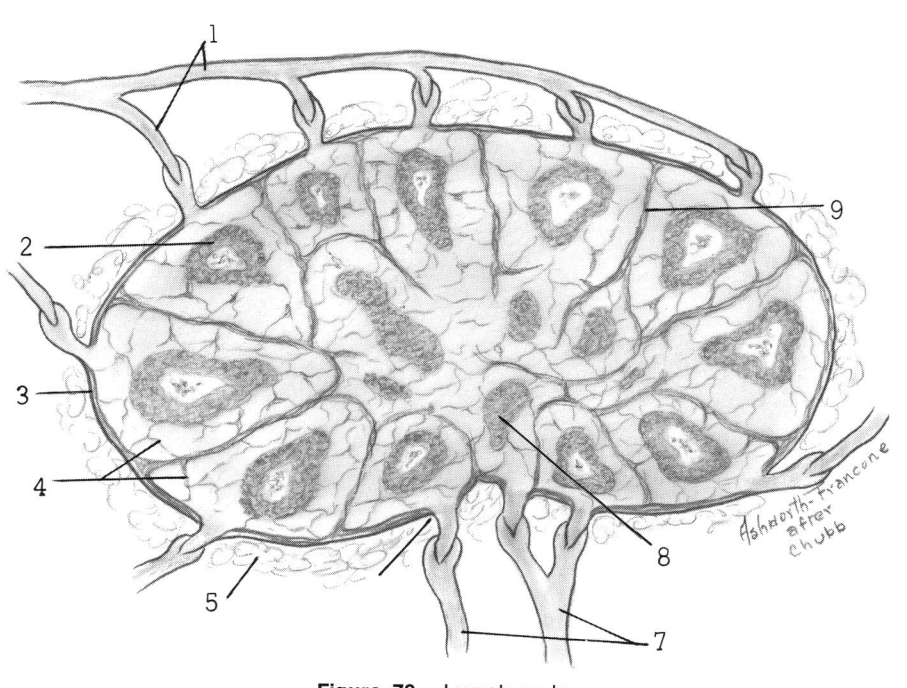

Figure 79. Lymph node.

PRACTICAL EXERCISES

ANATOMY AND PHYSIOLOGY QUESTIONS

1. List the functions of lymph nodes: _____

_____

_____

_____

2. Muscle action _____ (increases, decreases) lymph flow.

3. How do lymph vessels differ from blood vessels? _____

_____

_____

_____

CLINICAL QUESTIONS

1. Define elephantiasis: _____

_____

_____

_____

2. Define edema or "dropsy": _____

_____

_____

_____

3. Sometimes following severe infections in a hand, red streaks appear on the forearm. What are these red streaks? _____

_____

_____

_____

4. Since lymph channels help drain excess tissue fluid, what might you expect to find as a complication in a patient after a radical mastectomy (breast removal) with lymph node removal? _____

_____

_____

_____

Chapter 12

THE RESPIRATORY SYSTEM

Respiration is the transport of oxygen from the atmosphere to the cells and, in turn, the transport of carbon dioxide from the cells back to the atmosphere. Respiration is so vital that without it death ensues within a few minutes.

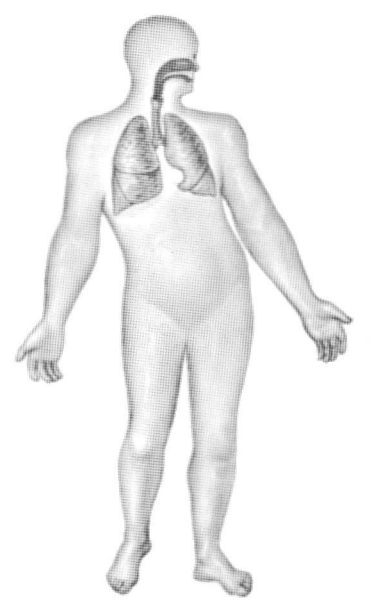

ANATOMY OF THE RESPIRATORY SYSTEM

EXPERIMENT A: Gross and Microscopic Examination of the Respiratory System of the Sheep or Other Animal

PHYSIOLOGY OF THE RESPIRATORY SYSTEM

EXPERIMENT B: Mechanics of Respiration
EXPERIMENT C: Relationship Between Carbon Dioxide Content of Blood and Rate and Depth of Respiration
EXPERIMENT D: Auscultation of Respiratory Sounds
EXPERIMENT E: Ciliary Movement in the Trachea
PRACTICAL EXERCISES

ANATOMY OF THE RESPIRATORY SYSTEM

EXPERIMENT A: Gross and Microscopic Examination of the Respiratory System of the Sheep or Other Animal

References:
   J & F, Ch. 12; appropriate chapters in Greisheimer, Kimber et al., Anthony, Guyton, Reith et al., King & Showers, Dienhart, Chaffee & Greisheimer.

Materials:
   1. Fresh or preserved sheep lungs with trachea (or other suitable animal respiratory system)
   2. Dissecting instruments and tray
   3. Sections of trachea and lung

Objective: To demonstrate the major structural characteristics of the respiratory system.

Procedure:
   1. Using references above locate larynx in your neck.
      a. Find and feel the thyroid cartilage
      b. Find and feel the cricoid cartilage
   2. Gross structure of the animal larynx (use references above).
      a. Note the lidlike (flaplike) opening into the larynx. What is it
         called? _____

b. Identify the major laryngeal cartilages (thyroid, cricoid).
   (1) Which structure prevents material from being aspirated into
       the larynx? _____
   (2) Which cartilage forms the "Adam's apple"? _____
c. Cut through the posterior wall of the larynx so that the interior of
   the larynx can be clearly seen. Name the opening between the
   vocal cords: _____
d. Label Figure 80 with the following terms:

Vocal fold	Frontal air sinus
Cricoid cartilage	Superior conchae
Epiglottis	Middle conchae
Palatine tonsil	Inferior conchae
Pharynx	Thyroid cartilage
Sphenoidal air sinus	Trachea

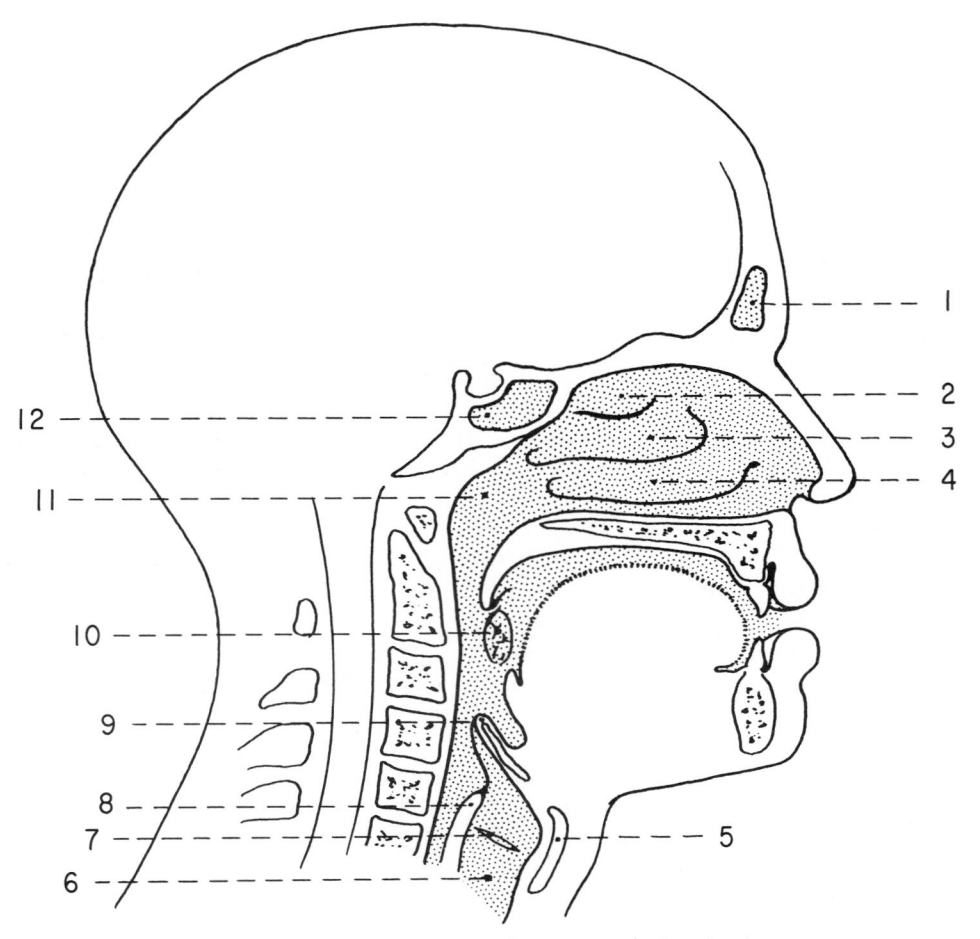

Figure 80. Cross section of upper respiratory tract.

3. Gross structure of animal trachea:
   a. Feel the cartilaginous rings. List the functions of these rings: _____

_____

_____

_____

   b. What fills in the posterior open part of the tracheal "U-shaped cartilages? _____

_____

   c. Feel the lining of the trachea. The inner layer of this membrane is composed of what type of epithelium? _____

_____

   d. Where is the trachea situated in relation to the esophagus (ventral, dorsal)? _____

_____

_____

4. Gross structure of animal bronchi and lungs:
   a. Note the number of lobes in the animal lung. How does this compare with human lungs?

	Human	Animal
Right lung	_____	_____
Left lung	_____	_____

   b. Name the serous membrane that cover the lungs: _____

_____

   c. What is the parietal layer applied to? _____

   d. What is the visceral layer of this membrane applied to? _____

_____

   e. Name the potential space between these two layers: _____

_____

_____

   f. Pinch a piece of fresh lung between your fingers. Describe the texture of lung tissue: _____

_____

   g. Continue the incision made in the larynx down the trachea into the bronchi, branching right and left.
      (1) Compare the cartilaginous structures of the bronchioles with the trachea: _____

_____

_____

      (2) Why are foreign bodies, when aspirated, usually found in the right mainstem bronchus? _____

_____

_____

h. Label Figure 81 with the following terms:

Lower lobe of lung	Thyroid cartilage
Alveolar sac	Cricoid cartilage
Respiratory bronchiole	Trachea
Alveolus	Left main bronchus
Oblique fissure	Upper lobe bronchus
Horizontal fissure	Lower lobe bronchus
Right upper lobe bronchus	Oblique fissure

5. Examine sections of trachea and lung tissue. Identify cartilage and smooth muscle in the trachea section. Identify alveolar duct and alveoli in the lung sections.

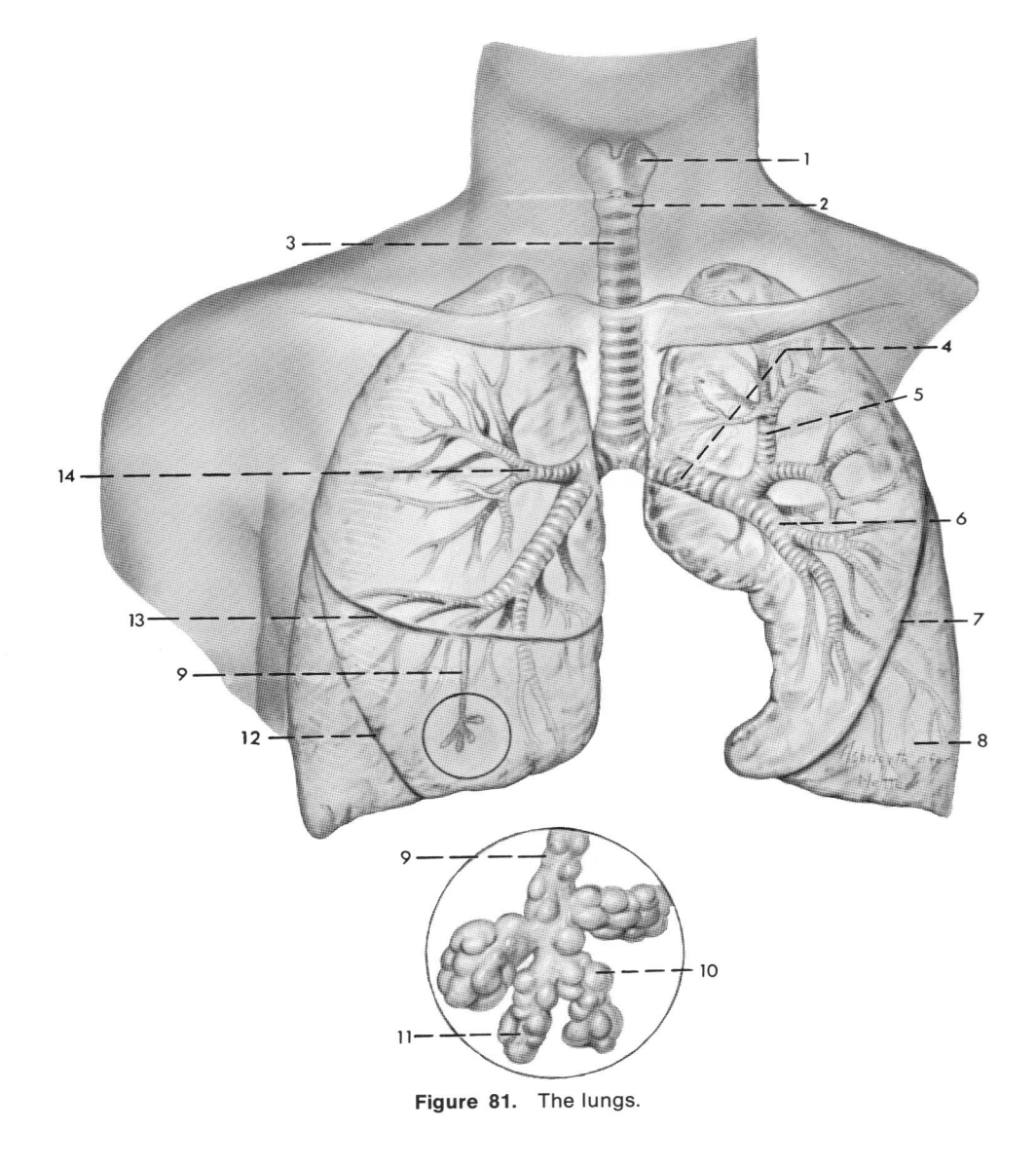

Figure 81. The lungs.

PHYSIOLOGY OF THE RESPIRATORY SYSTEM

EXPERIMENT B: Mechanics of Respiration

References:
>   J & F, Ch. 12; appropriate chapters in Greisheimer, Kimber et al., Anthony, Guyton, Reith et al., King & Showers, Dienhart, Chaffee & Greisheimer.

Materials:
>   Spirometer

Procedure:

1. When the diaphragm contracts, it _____ (ascends, descends). This _____ (increases, decreases) the volume of the thoracic cavity.

2. Which muscles are used during normal, quiet inspiration? _____

_____

_____

3. Muscular contractions cause the thorax to _____ (increase, decrease) in size, during inspiration. This size change causes a(n) _____ (increase, decrease) in the intrathoracic pressure. Since the pressure in the lung is now less than atmospheric pressure, air moves _____ (in, out).

4. Normal expiration is primarily a matter of relaxation, while forced expiration calls into play what muscles? _____

_____

_____

5. During normal expiration, the thorax _____ (increases, decreases) in size as a result of muscular relaxation, gravity, and elastic recoil of the lungs. This causes a(n) _____ (increase, decrease) in the intrathroacic pressure. Since the pressure within the lung is now _____ (more, less) than atmospheric, air moves _____ (in, out).

6. If the intrapleural pressure should become equal to atmospheric pressure (as in a pneumothorax), what would happen to the lung?

_____

_____

7. Measure your tidal air volume by taking an ordinary breath or expiration into a spirometer. Result: _____ cc.

8. Define expiratory reserve, inspiratory reserve, and vital capacity.

_____

_____

_____

9. Measure, by using a spirometer, your expiratory reserve _____ cc. Inspiratory reserve _____ cc. Vital capacity _____ cc.

EXPERIMENT C: Relationship Between Carbon Dioxide Content of Blood and Rate and Depth of Respiration

References:

J & F, Ch. 15; appropriate chapters in Greisheimer, Kimber et al., Anthony, Guyton, Reith et al., King & Showers, Dienhart, Chaffee & Greisheimer.

Materials:

Paper bag

Procedure:

1. Count subject's normal respiration rate for 1 minute (breaths/min.) and note depth as the subject sits quietly.

Rate: _____

Depth: _____

2. Have subject hyperventilate by breathing deeply and rapidly for 2 minutes. Immediately following hyperventilation, count respirations and note their depth for 1 minute.

Rate: _____

Depth: _____

3. Have subject rest to reach control level obtained in Procedure 1 above.

4. Next have subject hyperventilate into a closed system such as a spirometer or a paper bag held tightly over mouth and nose for 2 minutes. Immediately after, count respirations for 1 minute and note their depth.

Rate: _____

Depth: _____

5. Observations:

a. Does hyperventilation increase or decrease blood carbon dioxide content? _____

_____

b. Describe the relationship between blood carbon dioxide content and the rate and depth of respirations. _____

_____

_____

EXPERIMENT D: Auscultation of Respiratory Sounds

References:

Appropriate chapters in Greisheimer, Kimber et al.

Materials:

Stethoscope

Objective: To become acquainted with respiratory sounds.

Procedure:

1. During respiration, characteristic sounds can be heard over the chest. There are two classes of sounds:

    a. *Bronchial:* Place a stethoscope low over the larynx or the trachea and during quiet respiration a low inspiratory sound is heard, corresponding closely with the sound produced by breathing through the mouth held in a position to pronounce "h" or "ch." Is the sound heard during both inspiration and expiration?

    _____

    Place the stethoscope over the course of the trachea and bronchi, and note how far away the bronchial note can be heard. Does rapid, deep respiration increase this sound? _____

    b. *Vesicular:* Place the stethoscope over the right fifth intercostal space during quiet respiration. A gentle sound will be heard, resembling that made by breathing through the lips in a position to pronounce "f."

    Is this an inspiratory or expiratory sound? _____

    Is the sound altered during force respiration? _____

2. Whispered voice

    a. While the subject whispers "one, two, three," apply the stethoscope to symmetrical points on the thorax.

    b. Solidification of the lung makes these sounds clearer and higher pitched. This often aids the doctor in his diagnosis.

EXPERIMENT E: Ciliary Movement in the Trachea

References:

Appropriate chapters in Greisheimer, Kimber et al., Anthony, Reith et al., Dienhart, Chaffee & Greisheimer.

Materials:

1. Frog
2. Cork
3. Scalpel
3. Ether

Objective: To observe ciliary movement in the trachea.

Procedure:

1. Anesthetize the frog (follow procedure in Chapter 1, Experiment C).

2. Remove the lower jaw of the frog with scissors and make a slit down the ventral side of the trachea. Keep the surface of the trachea moist with Ringer's solution.

3. Place a very small piece of cork (a 1 mm. cube) above the part of the trachea where it begins to divide into two portions. Note the direction in which the cilia move.

4. Describe what you observe: _____

_____

_____

_____

PRACTICAL EXERCISES

CLINICAL QUESTIONS

1. Would it be possible to commit suicide by holding your breath? _____
Why? _____
_____
_____

2. Why may a doctor order high concentrations of carbon dioxide inhalations for his postoperative patients? _____
_____
_____

3. Briefly explain these terms:
   a. Apnea: _____
   _____

   b. Anoxia: _____
   _____

   c. Asphyxia: _____
   _____

   d. Cheyne-Stokes respiration: _____
   _____

   e. Orthopnea: _____
   _____

Chapter 13

THE DIGESTIVE SYSTEM

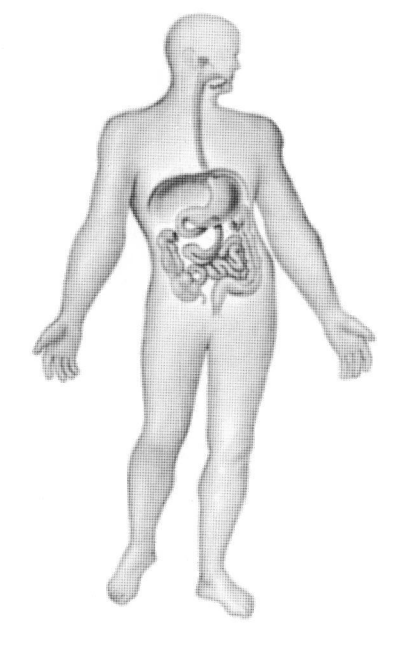

The materials used by the body for energy and for the maintenance and rebuilding of tissues are carbohydrates, fats, and proteins. However, these cannot be absorbed in their natural form through the gastrointestinal mucosa and, for this reason, are useless without the preliminary process of digestion.

ANATOMY OF THE DIGESTIVE SYSTEM
EXPERIMENT A: Digestive Organs

PHYSIOLOGY OF THE DIGESTIVE SYSTEM
EXPERIMENT B: Chemical Changes on Carbohydrates
by Saliva
EXPERIMENT C: Digestive Enzymes
EXPERIMENT D: Deglutition
PRACTICAL EXERCISES

ANATOMY OF THE DIGESTIVE SYSTEM

EXPERIMENT A: Digestive Organs

References:
J & F, Ch. 13; appropriate chapters in Greisheimer, Kimber et al., Anthony, Guyton, Reith et al., King & Showers, Dienhart, Chaffee & Greisheimer.

Materials:
1. Laboratory animal (a preserved animal from earlier dissection is preferable here)
2. Jar
3. Ether or nembutal
4. Cotton
5. Normal saline (see appendix)
6. Gauze sponges

Objective: To demonstrate digestive organs in an intact animal.

Procedure:
1. Anesthetize a laboratory animal (follow procedure in Chapter 1, Experiment C (skip to 5 if preserved animal is used).
2. Make a midline incision from the sternum to the pubis, cutting through the skin and fascia, and being careful not to injure underlying structures.
3. Keep animal moist with normal saline.
4. Place gauze sponges soaked in hot physiological saline over a section of intestine. What happens? _____

5. Using the references listed above, identify the following parts of the digestive system.

Parotid gland

Pharynx

Stomach

Pancreas

Jejunum

Descending colon

Sigmoid colon

Anus

Rectum

Appendix

Ileum

Ascending colon

Transverse colon

Duodenum

Common bile duct

Gallbladder

Sublingual gland

Esophagus

Liver

Submaxillary gland

Hepatic duct

Spleen

Pancreatic duct

Cystic duct

Incisors

Canine teeth

Premolars

Molars

Hard palate

Soft palate

Uvula

6. Label Figures 82 through 85 with the terms listed above and below.

Neck of tooth

Root of tooth

Dental nerve

Vessels to tooth

Cementum

Pulp cavity

Crown

Pulp

Dentin

Enamel

Root canal

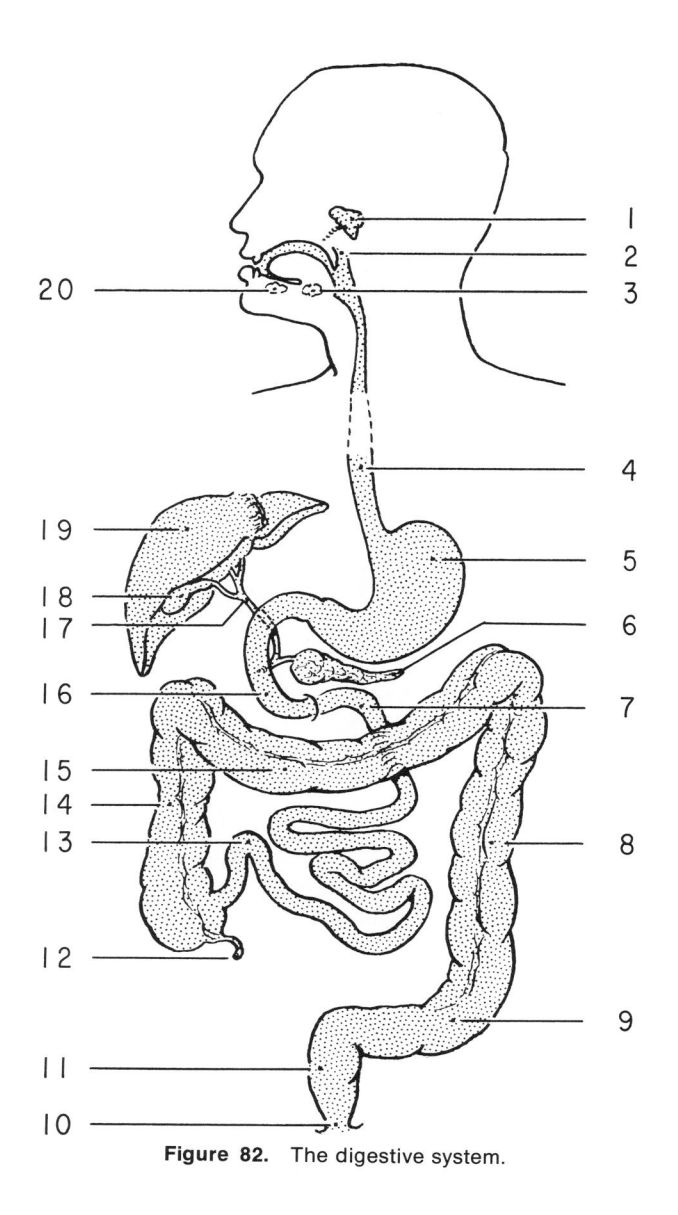

Figure 82. The digestive system.

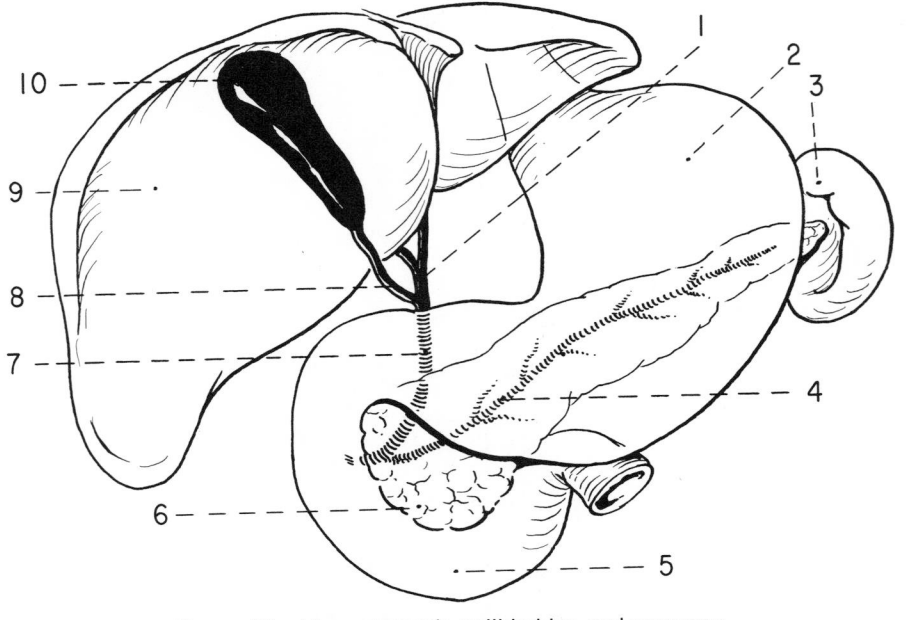

Figure 83.   Liver, stomach, gallbladder, and pancreas.

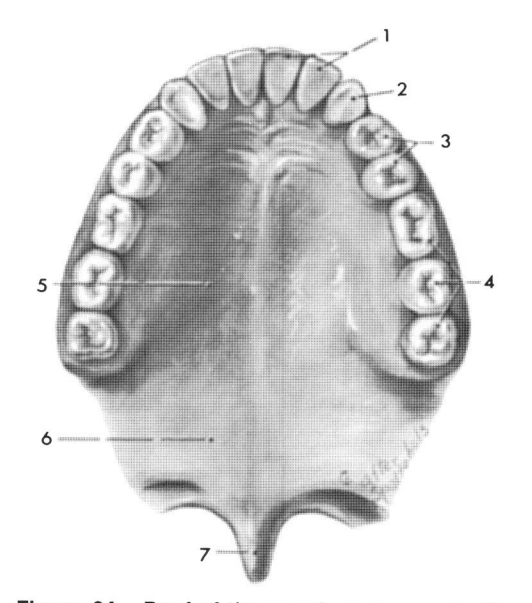

Figure 84. Roof of the mouth and upper teeth.

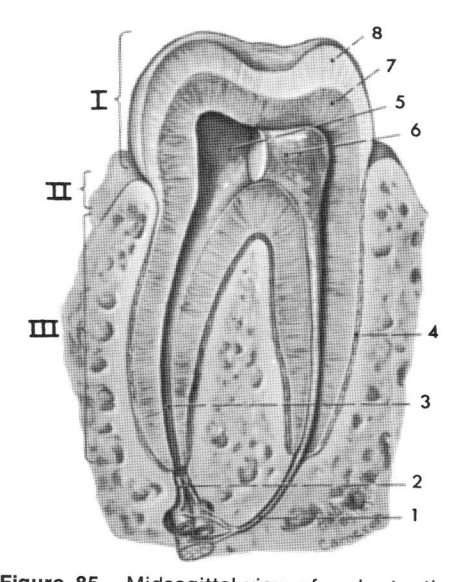

Figure 85. Midsagittal view of molar tooth.

PHYSIOLOGY OF THE DIGESTIVE SYSTEM

EXPERIMENT B: Chemical Changes on Carbohydrates by Saliva

References:

J & F, Ch. 13; appropriate chapters in Greisheimer, Kimber et al., Anthony, Guyton, Reith et al., King & Showers, Dienhart, Chaffee & Greisheimer.

Materials:

1. Cornstarch
2. Water
3. Lugol's iodine solution (see appendix)
4. Benedict's solution (see appendix)

Objective: To show that saliva breaks starch into less complex carbohydrates.

Procedure:

1. Make a thin paste by mixing a half teaspoonful of cornstarch with a little cold water, adding it to 100 ml. of boiling water, and stirring while boiling for 2 or 3 minutes. Cool.

2. Put 5 ml. of this starch solution in a test tube. Add 1 drop of Lugol's iodine solution. (This is the standard test for starch.) What is the color change?

_____

_____

3. Put 10 ml. of the starch solution into a test tube and add two or more drops of saliva. Set in a water bath at 37 to 40° C. It should take the solution about half an hour to become colorless. What does this indicate? _____

_____

4. Add about 4 drops of this colorless solution to 5 ml. of Benedict's solution. Boil 2 minutes and cool slowly. A red, yellow, or green precipitate indicates the presence of glucose.

5. Discuss the results in terms of enzymatic action._____

_____

_____

EXPERIMENT C: Digestive Enzymes

References:
> J & F, Ch. 13; appropriate chapters in Greisheimer, Kimber et al., Anthony, Guyton, Reith et al., King & Showers, Dienhart, Chaffee & Greisheimer.

Procedure:
> 1. Fill in the following chart:

DIGESTIVE JUICES AND THEIR ENZYMES	FOOD DIGESTED	PRODUCT
1. Saliva		
a. Ptyalin		
b. Maltose		
2. Gastric juice		
a. Pepsinogen		
b. Lipase		
3. Bile		
a. No enzyme		
4. Pancreatic juice		
a. Pepsinogen		
b. Lipase		
c. Amylase		
d. Carboxypeptidase		
5. Intestinal Juice		
a. Maltase		
b. Sucrase		
c. Lactase		
d. Protease		

EXPERIMENT D: Deglutition

References:

J & F, Ch. 13; appropriate chapters in Greisheimer, Kimber et al., Anthony, Guyton, Reith et al., King & Showers, Dienhart, Chaffee & Greisheimer.

Materials:

1. Stethoscope
2. Water

Objective: To understand the act of swallowing.

Procedure:

1. Using the references listed above, find out if swallowing is an active, reflex, or active and reflex process by taking a mouthful of water and lying with your head hanging down across a laboratory table. Swallow the water. Describe the result. _____

_____

_____

2. Place a stethoscope below the lower end of the sternum of a standing subject who will swallow 5 large mouthfuls of water rapidly while you listen. Describe the stomach cardiac valve sound produced. _____

_____

_____

PRACTICAL EXERCISES

ANATOMY AND PHYSIOLOGY QUESTIONS

1. Which of the following elicit the most calories per gram when metabolized?

  a. Fats: _____

  b. Carbohydrates: _____

  c. Proteins: _____

2. Why is bile essential (it contains no enzymes)? _____

_____

_____

3. What are the soluble and diffusible end products of digestion from carbohydrates? _____

_____

From proteins? _____

_____

From fats? _____

CLINICAL QUESTIONS

1. List three digestive mechanisms found in newborn babies and young infants that differ from older persons: _____

_____

_____

2. Which types of food would be most suitable for young babies?

  a. Carbohydrates: _____

  b. Proteins: _____

  c. Fats: _____

3. If a patient has advanced liver disease, such as cirrhosis, what would be the implications of this problem with regard to digestibility and absorbability of different foods? _____

_____

_____

4. Would you think that total removal of a stomach would be compatible with life? _____ Why? _____

_____

_____

5. Why does a child need more calories per pound of body weight and a higher proportion of protein than an adult? _____

_____

_____

Chapter 14

THE URINARY SYSTEM

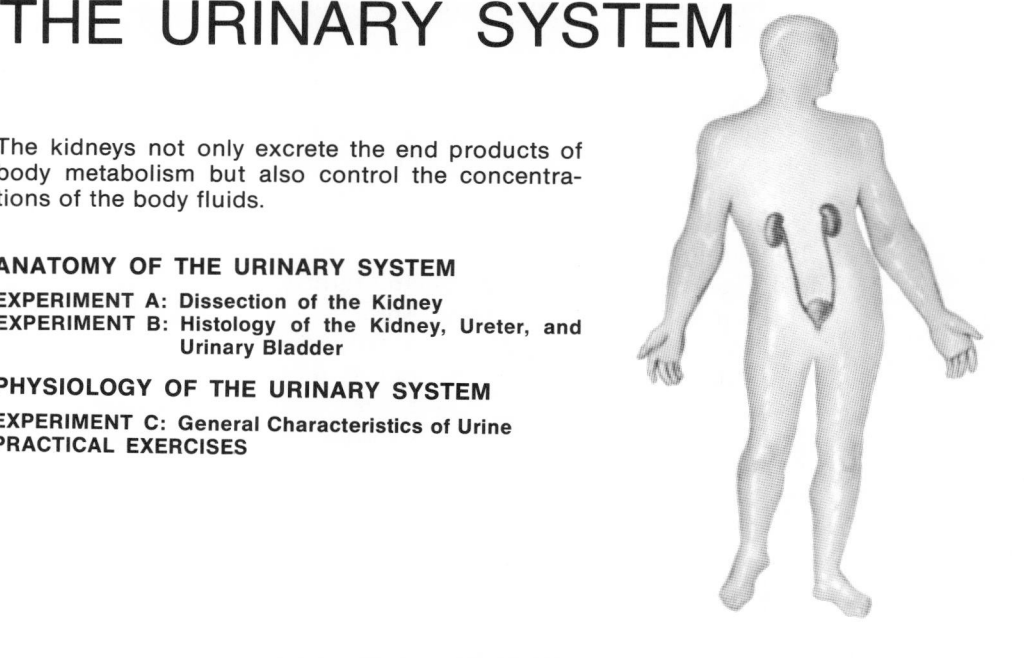

The kidneys not only excrete the end products of body metabolism but also control the concentrations of the body fluids.

ANATOMY OF THE URINARY SYSTEM
EXPERIMENT A: Dissection of the Kidney
EXPERIMENT B: Histology of the Kidney, Ureter, and Urinary Bladder

PHYSIOLOGY OF THE URINARY SYSTEM
EXPERIMENT C: General Characteristics of Urine
PRACTICAL EXERCISES

ANATOMY OF THE URINARY SYSTEM

EXPERIMENT A: Dissection of the Kidney

References:
    J & F, Ch. 14; appropriate chapters in Greisheimer, Kimber et al., Anthony, Reith et al., King & Showers, Dienhart, Chaffee & Greisheimer.
Materials:
    1. Preserved kidneys (dogs, sheep, pig)
    2. Dissecting instruments and tray
Objective: To see the gross structural features which characterize the kidneys.
Procedure:
    1. Using the references listed above, note the large amount of adipose tissue which surrounds the kidney. What purpose is served by this fat? _____
_____

_____

    2. Name the structure that carries urine from the kidney to the bladder:
_____ It is lined with what kind of membrane?
_____

_____

    3. With a sharp knife make a longitudinal incision around the convex border of the kidney to the pelvis of the kidney. (See Fig. 86)
    4. Note the granular renal cortex. What microscopic structures are located in the cortex? _____
In the medulla? _____

5. Distinguish between the renal artery and the renal vein.

6. Using the references listed above find the following on the preserved
kidney.

Inferior vena cava   Renal artery
Cortex   Ureter
Medulla   Minor calyx
Major calyx   Pelvis
Opening of calyx   Papilla
Pyramid   Fibrous capsule
Renal vein

7. Label Fig. 86 and 87 in the following terms:

Inferior vena cava   Aorta
Cortex   Renal artery
Medulla   Left kidney
Minor calyx   Ureter
Major calyx   Bladder
Pelvis   Prostate gland
Opening of calyx   Urethra
Papilla   External iliac artery
Pyramid   and vein
Fibrous capsule   Internal iliac artery
Renal vein   and vein

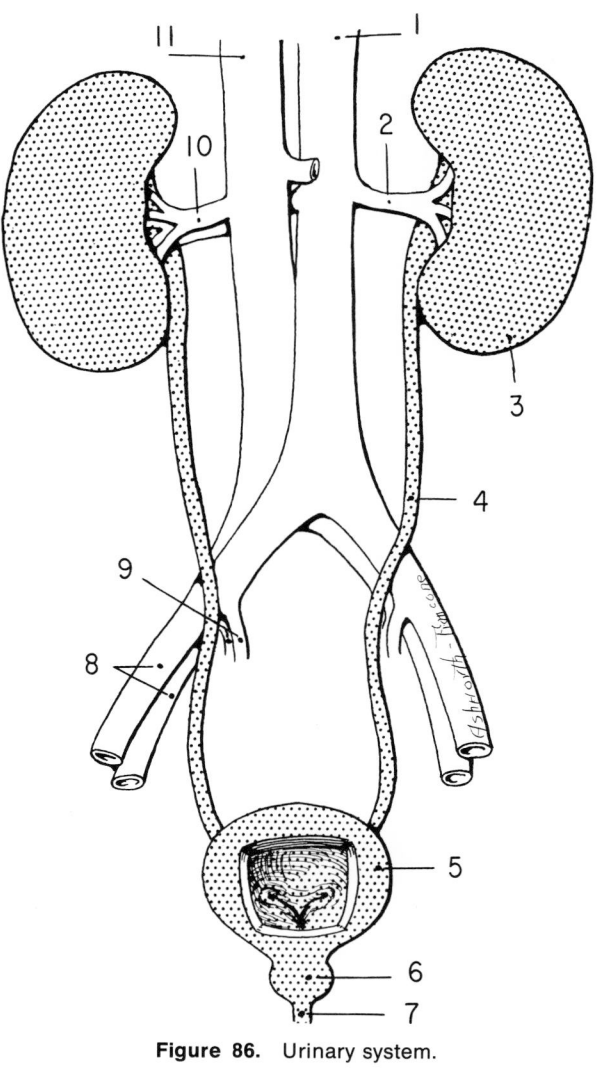

Figure 86. Urinary system.

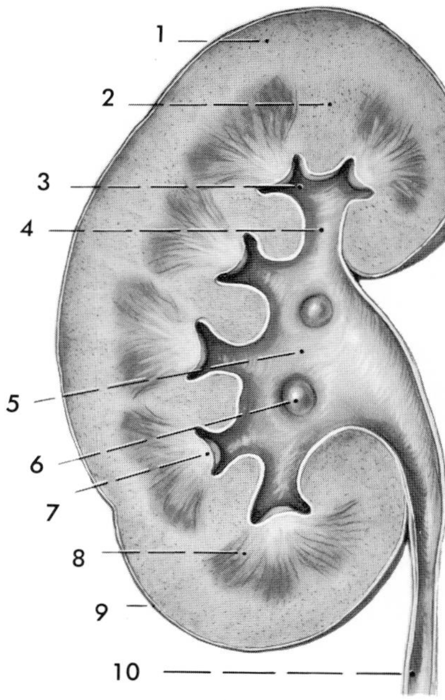

Figure 87. Cross section of the kidney.

EXPERIMENT B: Histology of the Kidney, Ureter, and Urinary Bladder

References:

J & F, Ch. 14; appropriate chapters in Greisheimer, Kimber et al., Anthony, Reith et al., King & Showers, Dienhart, Chaffee & Greisheimer, Ham & Leeson.

Materials:

1. Histologic sections of kidney, ureter, and urinary bladder tissue
2. Microscope

Objective: To demonstrate the microscopic structure of the kidney, ureter, and urinary bladder.

Procedure:

1. Using references above examine the sections of kidney and locate the following structures.

Interlobular artery   Descending loop of Henle
Efferent arteriole   Ascending loop of Henle
Afferent arteriole   Interlobular vein
Glomerular (Bowman's)   Distal convoluted tubule
   capsule   Collecting duct
Proximal convoluted tubule

2. Label Fig. 88 with the above terms.

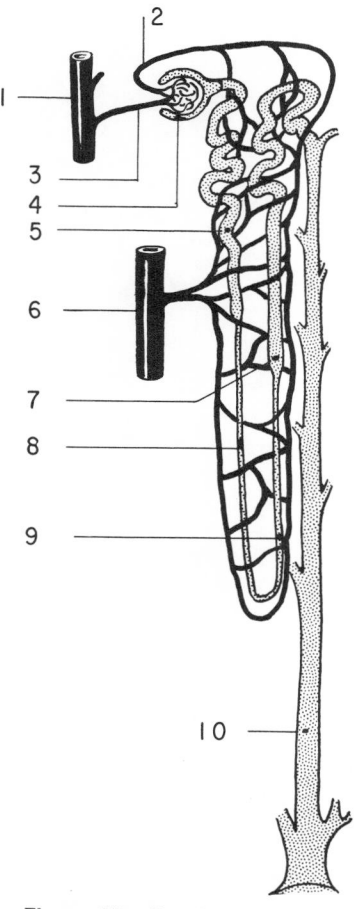

Figure 88. Detail of a nephron.

3. Examine section of ureter and urinary bladder. Identify the following:
   Ureter:
   Adipose tissue
   Circular muscle layer
   Longitudinal muscle layer
   Lumen
   Transitional epithelium
   Veins
   Arteries
   Urinary bladder:
   Smooth muscle
   Connective tissue
   Transitional epithelium
   Folds of mucosa
   Capillaries

PHYSIOLOGY OF THE URINARY SYSTEM

EXPERIMENT C: General Characteristics of Urine

References:

J & F, Ch. 14; appropriate chapters in Greisheimer, Kimber et al., Anthony, Guyton, Reith et al., King & Showers, Dienhart, Chaffee & Greisheimer.

Materials:

1. Samples of urine
2. "Hema-Combistix" test paper
3. Urine hydrometer

Objective: To observe general characteristics of urine.

Procedure:

1. Using the references listed above, carefully place a urine hydrometer in a tube of urine and read the specific gravity from the scale. Record in chart below.

2. Using a test strip of "Hema-Combistix" test paper check the urine sample for pH, glucose, protein, and blood. Record in chart below.

3. Examine urine samples and note color, and appearance (clear, cloudy, or sedimented).

4. Fill in the following chart.

	normal values	*test samples*
a. Amount (per 24-hour period):		
b. Color:		
c. Clarity:		
d. Odor:		
e. Specific gravity:		
f. Albumin:		
g. Sugar:		
h. Blood:		
i. Mucous material:		

PRACTICAL EXERCISES

ANATOMY AND PHYSIOLOGY QUESTIONS

1. From the following list of lettered transport mechanisms, pick one or more mechanism for the exchange of substances between the tubular filtrate and the blood:

    a. Active transport   d. Osmosis

    b. Diffusion   e. Reabsorption

    c. Filtration   f. Secretion

_____

_____

Substances	Transport Mechanism
Sodium ions	_____
Chloride	_____
Potassium ions	_____
Glucose	_____

2. Anatomically trace a drop of waste material from Bowman's capsule to the urethra. _____

_____

_____

_____

CLINICAL QUESTIONS

1. What is the function of ADH (antidiuretic hormone)? _____

_____

_____

2. Micturition refers to: _____

_____

_____

3. After hemorrhage, what is one compensating mechanism to suppress urine formation? _____

_____

_____

4. Define catheterization: _____

_____

_____

5. What is the general function of diuretic drugs? _____

_____

_____

6. Discuss the character and composition of urine from individuals with diabetes insipidus and diabetes mellitus. _____

_____

_____

Chapter 15

THE ENDOCRINE SYSTEM

The glands of the endocrine system work in harmony with the nervous system to control and coordinate all the activities of the body.

ANATOMY OF THE ENDOCRINE SYSTEM

EXPERIMENT A: Location and Structure of Endocrine Glands
EXPERIMENT B: Histology of Endocrine Gland Tissues

PHYSIOLOGY OF THE ENDOCRINE SYSTEM

EXPERIMENT C: Endocrine Hormones and Function
EXPERIMENT D: Insulin Shock (Demonstration)
PRACTICAL EXERCISES

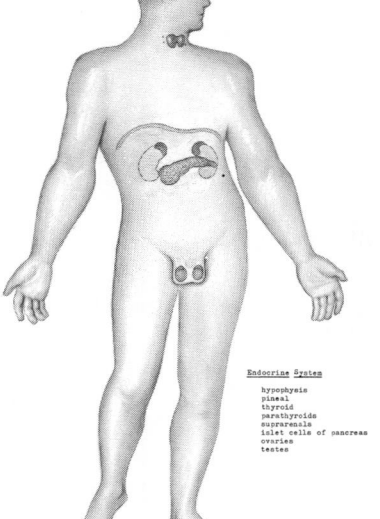

Endocrine System

hypophysis
pineal
thyroid
parathyroids
suprarenals
islet cells of pancreas
ovaries
testes

ANATOMY OF THE ENDOCRINE SYSTEM

EXPERIMENT A: Location and Structure of Endocrine Glands

References:

> J & F, Ch. 14; appropriate chapters in Greisheimer, Kimber et al., Anthony, Reith et al., King & Showers, Chaffee & Greisheimer.

Materials:

> 1. Model of human torso
> 2. Human skull
> 3. Embalmed cat or other mammal (demonstration)

Objective: To visualize the anatomic location of the various endocrine glands and their major structural characteristics.

Procedure:

> 1. Using the references listed above, model of a human torso, and the dissected embalmed cat; show the location and structure of the following endocrine glands:

Hypophysis (pituitary)	Ovaries
Thyroid and parathyroid	Testes
Pancreatic islets (Langerhans)	Pineal gland
Suprarenals	

> 2. Label Figure 89 with the above terms.

> 3. Examine the human skull and locate the sella turcica of the sphenoid bone in which the hypophysis is located. If a human brain is available, study the shape, size, consistency, and color of the hypophysis.

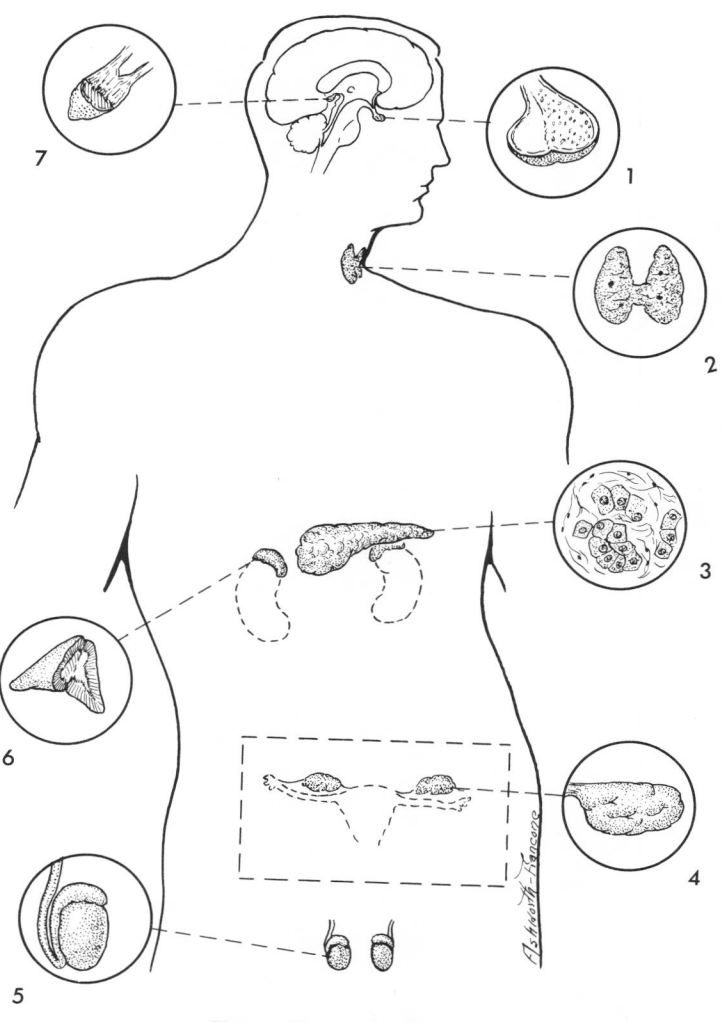

Figure 89. Endocrine glands.

EXPERIMENT B: Histology of Endocrine Gland Tissues

References:

    J & F, Ch. 15; appropriate chapters in Greisheimer, Kimber et al., Anthony, Reith et al., King & Showers, Dienhart, Chaffee & Greisheimer, Ham & Leeson.

Materials:

    Histologic section of endocrine tissues (ovaries and testes will be studied in Chapter 17).

Objective: To demonstrate endocrine glands through histologic examination.

Procedure:

    1. Using the references listed above, examine the sections provided. Find the following:

> *Pituitary (hypophysis)*
> > Pars anterior
> > Pars intermedia
> > Pars nervosa
>
> *Thyroid*
> > Follicle capillaries
> > Colloid
> > Cuboidal epithelium
> > Parathyroids (try to locate them)
>
> *Adrenals (suprarenals)*
> > Capsule
> > Cortex
> > Medulla
>
> *Pancreatic islets (islets of Langerhans)*
> > Find the islets in a section of a pancreas
>
> *Pineal body (if available)*
> > Septum
> > Parenchyma
> > Brain sand (calcified bodies)

PHYSIOLOGY OF THE ENDOCRINE SYSTEM

EXPERIMENT C: Endocrine Hormones and Function

References:

J & F, Ch. 15; appropriate chapters in Greisheimer, Kimber et al., Anthony, Guyton, Reith et al., King & Showers, Dienhart, Chaffee & Greisheimer.

Procedure: Fill in on the following chart the function of the stated hormones:

GLAND AND HORMONE	FUNCTION
Thyroid	
1. Thyroid hormone	
Parathyroids	
1. Parathyroid hormone	
Pancreatic Islets	
1. Insulin	
2. Glucagon	
Suprarenal Glands	
A. Cortex	
1. Mineralocorticoids (aldosterone)	
2. Glucocorticoids (cortisol)	
3. Androgens	
B. Medulla	
1. Epinephrine (adrenalin)	
2. Norepinephrine (noradrenalin)	
Ovaries	
1. Estrogen	
2. Progesterone	
Testes	
1. Testosterone	
Pineal Gland	
1. Unknown	
Placenta	
1. Estrogen	
2. Progesterone	
3. Chorionic gonadotropin	
Hypophysis	
Neurohypophysis	
1. Oxytocin	
2. Vasopressin	
Adenohypophysis	
1. STH	
2. ACTH	
3. TSH	
4. FSH	
5. LH	
6. ICSH	
7. MSH	

EXPERIMENT D: Insulin Shock (Demonstration)

References:

J & F, Ch. 15; appropriate chapters in Greisheimer, Kimber et al., Anthony, Guyton, Reith et al., King & Showers, Dienhart, Chaffee & Greisheimer.

Materials:

1. Fish (goldfish, sunfish, etc.)
2. 1 ml. beaker
3. Commercial insulin (40 units/ml.)
4. Glucose

Objective: To understand hormonal effect.

Procedure:

1. Add 10 to 15 drops of commercial insulin to about 200 ml. of water.
2. Place fish in beaker and observe for convulsions or coma.
3. Remove fish and place in beaker of water containing about 200 ml. of water to which has been added a teaspoon of glucose. Observe for recovery.

4. Explain what took place. _____

_____

_____

_____

PRACTICAL EXERCISES

ANATOMY AND PHYSIOLOGY QUESTIONS

1. Distinguish between an exocrine gland and an endocrine gland: _____
_____
_____
_____

2. Define hormones: _____
_____
_____
_____

3. List the ways in which the endocrine glands and the nervous system are related: _____
_____
_____
_____

CLINICAL QUESTIONS

1. A 50 year old woman has been admitted to the hospital for treatment of Graves' disease (exophthalmic goiter). The surgeon plans to perform a subtotal thyroidectomy.

a. What is an exophthalmic goiter? _____
_____
_____

b. What is a subtotal thyroidectomy? _____
_____
_____

2. Briefly define the following:
a. Acromegaly: _____
_____

b. Cretinism: _____
_____

c. Myxedema: _____
_____

d. Rickets: _____
_____

e. Cushing's syndrome: _____
_____

3. In what way is a highly vascular blood supply important to an endocrine gland? _____

_____

_____

_____

Chapter 16

FLUIDS AND ELECTROLYTES

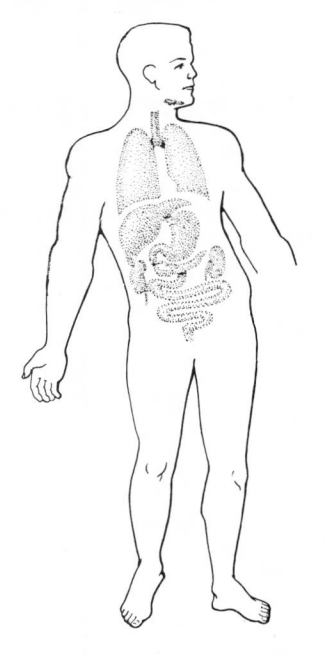

Water is the most abundant constituent of the body. It is a necessary component of cells, though it may be only loosely held together by covalent bonds. It provides the fluid within which the chemical reactions of the body take place and substances are transported.

Electrolytes are distributed in solution throughout all the body fluids, blood, lymph, intracellular fluids, digestive juices, and urine. Increased or decreased concentrations of any one electrolyte can often elicit very serious body malfunctions.

The cell membrane regulates the movement of materials into and out of the cell. Filtration, diffusion, osmosis, active transport, and pinocytosis are mechanisms by which cell membranes regulate the movement of materials.

EXPERIMENT A: Filtration
EXPERIMENT B: Diffusion
EXPERIMENT C: Osmosis
PRACTICAL EXERCISES

EXPERIMENT A: Filtration

References:
J & F, Ch. 16; appropriate chapters in Greisheimer, Kimber et al., Anthony, Guyton, Reith et al., King & Showers, Dienhart, Chaffee & Greisheimer.

Materials:
1. Powdered wood charcoal
2. Copper sulfate
3. Water
4. Funnel
5. Beaker
6. Filter paper

Objective: To demonstrate the principles of filtration.

Procedure:

1. Pour a mixture of charcoal powder, copper sulfate, and water through a piece of filter paper in a funnel draining into a beaker.

2. Which substances pass through the filter paper? _____

_____

Why? _____

_____

3. Discuss: _____

_____

_____

_____

EXPERIMENT B: Diffusion

References:

J & F, Ch. 16; appropriate chapters in Greisheimer, Kimber et al., Anthony, Guyton, Reith et al., King & Showers, Dienhart, Chaffee & Greisheimer.

Materials:

1. Potassium permanganate
2. Water
3. Sodium chloride
4. Egg albumen
5. Beaker
6. Dialysis tubing (or cellophane)
7. Concentrated nitric acid
8. 3 to 5% silver nitrate solution

Objective: To demonstrate the principle of diffusion.

Procedure:

1. Drop a crystal of potassium permanganate into a beaker of water. Observe this beaker at different times throughout the lab period.

    a. What happens? _____

_____

_____

2. A mixture of water, sodium chloride, and egg albumen is placed in a dialyzing bag. This preparation then is carefully placed in a beaker of distilled water. At the end of the lab period the instructor will test the two liquids for presence or absence of sodium chloride and egg albumen. For example, silver nitrate ($AgNO_3$) will react with sodium chloride to form a white precipitate of silver chloride. Concentrated nitric acid will coagulate the protein albumen.

    a. What was found in the cellophane bag? _____

_____

    b. What was found in the fluid surrounding the bag? _____

_____

    c. Explain briefly why this happened. _____

_____

_____

EXPERIMENT C: Osmosis (Fig. 90)

References:
> J & F, Ch. 16; appropriate chapters in Greisheimer, Kimber et al., Anthony, Guyton, Reith et al., King & Showers, Dienhart, Chaffee & Greisheimer.

Materials:
1. Dialysis tubing (or cellophane)
2. Water and beaker
3. 5% glucose solution (dextrose)
4. Methylene blue dye (see appendix)
5. Short stem thistle tube
6. Buret clamp

Objective: To show the principles of osmosis.

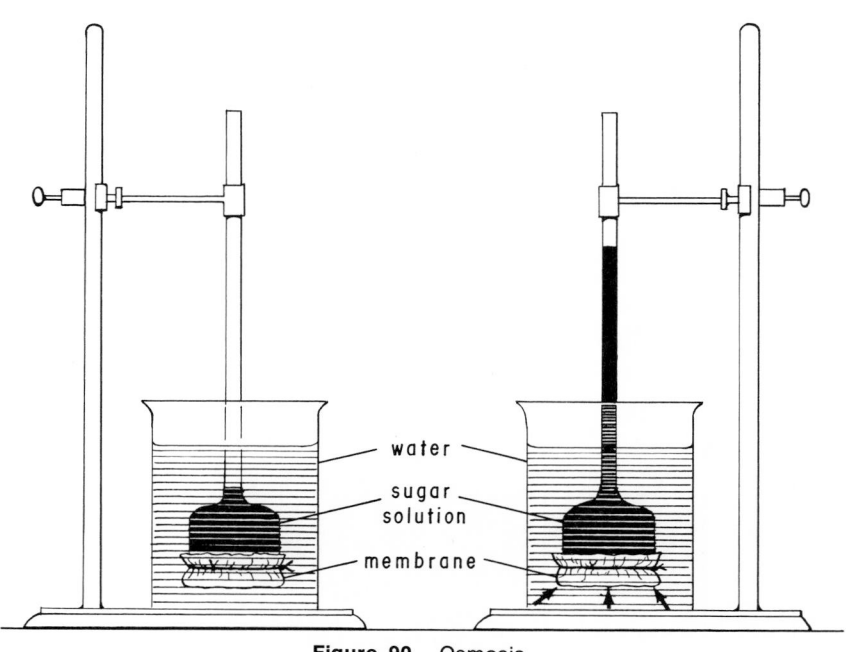

Figure 90. Osmosis.

Procedure:

1. Fill the bulb of a thistle tube with 5% glucose solution (add a small amount of methylene blue dye to the solution) by holding the tube with the bulb up and placing your finger over the small opening. Wet the cellophane membrane with water and with a rubber band fit it over the large end of the thistle tube. The fluid level in beaker and tube must be identical.

2. Place the tube (inverted) into a 250 cc. beaker of water and clamp securely to a ring stand.

    a. Examine the glass tubing at intervals. What happens and why?

_____

_____

_____

3. Red blood cells have a normal saline content of 0.9%. If red blood cells were placed in the following solutions what would happen:

    a. 0.9% saline: _____

    Why? _____

_____

    b. Distilled water: _____

    Why? _____

_____

    c. 25 per cent saline: _____

    Why? _____

_____

PRACTICAL EXERCISES

Define the following:

    1. Osmosis: _____

_____

    2. Diffusion: _____

_____

    3. Filtration: _____

_____

    4. An isotonic solution: _____

_____

    5. Hypotonic solution: _____

_____

    6. Hypertonic solution: _____

_____

    7. Hemolysis: _____

_____

    8. Crenation: _____

_____

    9. Active transport: _____

_____

   10. Pinocytosis: _____

_____

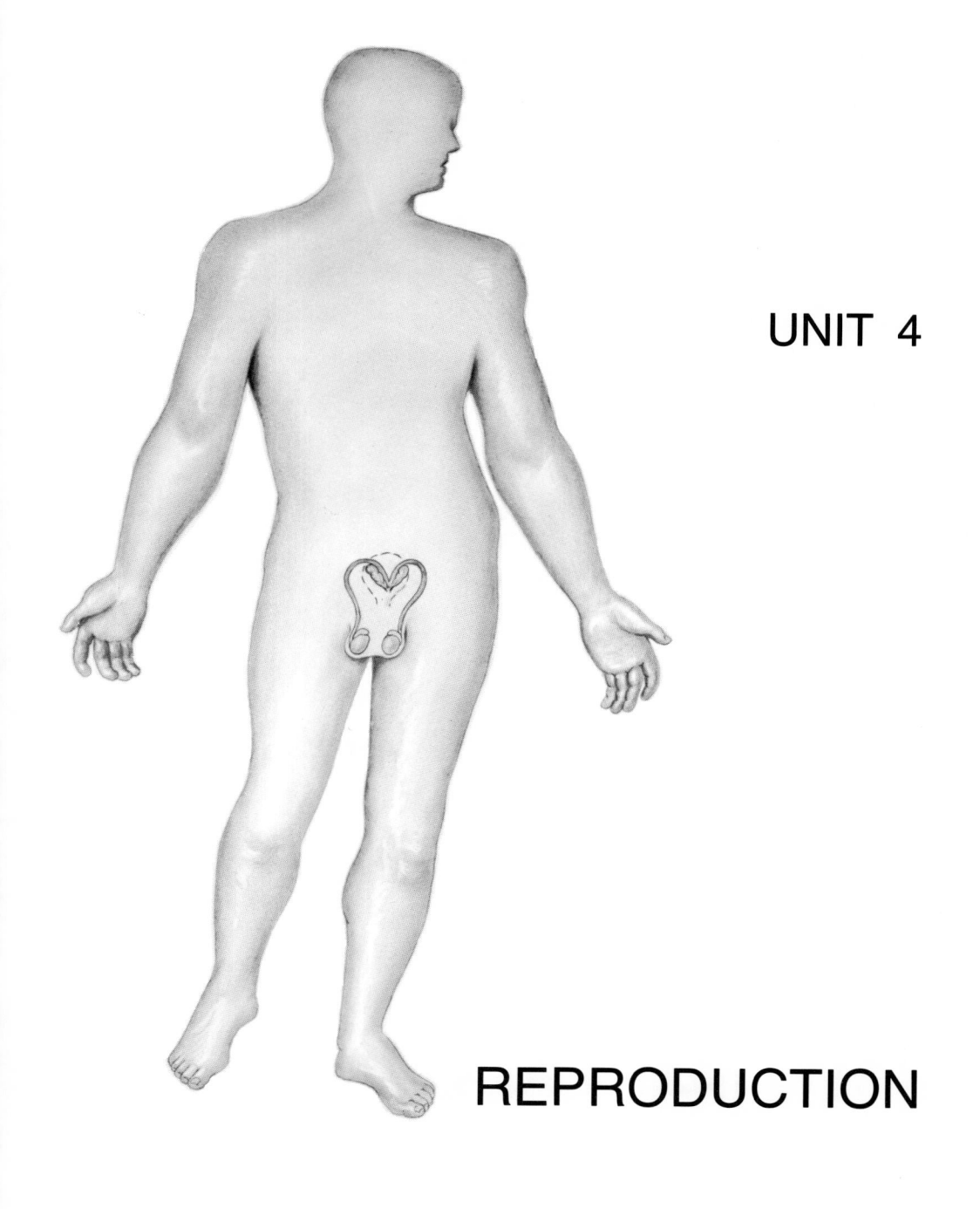

UNIT 4

REPRODUCTION

Chapter 17

THE REPRODUCTIVE SYSTEM

The two primary concerns of all living organisms are the maintenance of self and the perpetuation of the species. Sexual reproduction is the most common method of propagation. The reproductive system consists of primary and accessory sex organs. The primary organs are the paired gonads, ovaries in the female and testes in the male. After fertilization, the egg (zygote), under proper conditions and by a series of complicated processes, develops into an embryo.

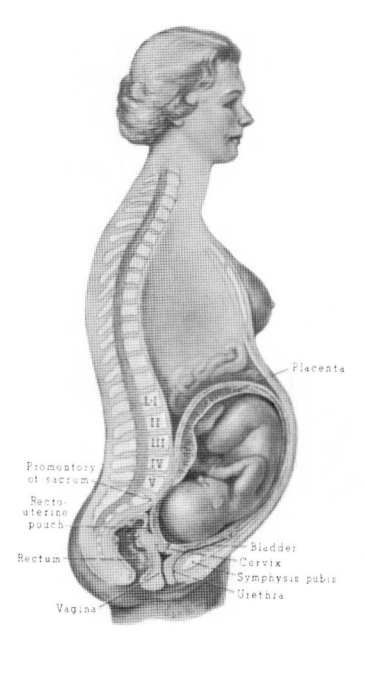

ANATOMY OF THE REPRODUCTIVE SYSTEM

EXPERIMENT A: **Male Reproductive System**
EXPERIMENT B: **Histology of the Testes and Penis**
EXPERIMENT C: **Female Reproductive System**
EXPERIMENT D: **Histology of the Ovary, Uterus, and Vagina**
EXPERIMENT E: **Mammary Glands (Optional)**

PHYSIOLOGY OF THE REPRODUCTIVE SYSTEM

EXPERIMENT F: **Gametogenesis (Meiosis—Demonstration)**
EXPERIMENT G: **Menstrual Cycle (Optional)**
EXPERIMENT H: **Biologic Tests for Pregnancy**

EMBRYOLOGY

EXPERIMENT I: **Pregnant Uterus and Embryological Development**
PRACTICAL EXERCISES

ANATOMY OF THE REPRODUCTIVE SYSTEM

EXPERIMENT A: Male Reproductive System

References:
J & F, Ch. 17; appropriate chapters in Greisheimer, Kimber et al., Anthony, Reith et al., King & Showers, Dienhart, Chaffee & Greisheimer.
Materials:
1. Embalmed male cat or other mammal (demonstration)
2. Model of male pelvis
3. Preserved and fresh scrotum and testes when available (demonstration)
4. Dissecting instruments and tray
Objective: To observe the general anatomic characteristics of the male reproductive system.

Procedure:

1. Using the references indicated above, examine model of male pelvis; dissected embalmed cat; preserved and fresh scrotum and testes. Identify the following structures.

Testis	Seminal vesicle
Urogenital diaphragm	Common ejaculatory duct
Bulbo spongiosus m.	Symphysis pubis
Bulbo urethral gland	Bladder
External anal sphincter	Corpus cavernosum
Anus	Ductus deferens
Anal canal	Epididymis
Prostate gland	Penile urethra
Coccyx	Glans penis
Rectum	Prepuce
Sacrum	Urethral meatus
Vertebral canal	Scrotum
Abdominal cavity	

2. Label Figure 91 with the above terms.

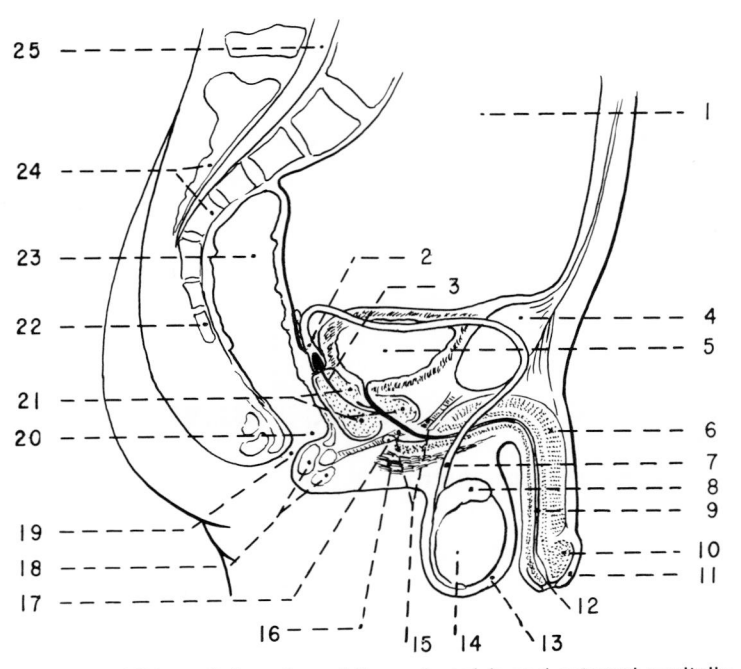

Figure 91. Midsaggital section of the male pelvis and external genitalia.

EXPERIMENT B: Histology of the Testes and Penis

References:

J & F, Ch. 17; appropriate chapters in Greisheimer, Kimber et al., Anthony, Guyton, Reith et al., King & Showers, Dienhart, Chaffee & Greisheimer, Ham & Leeson.

Materials:

1. Histologic sections of testicular and penile tissue
2. Microscope

Objective: To understand the microscopic structure, gross structure, and function of testes and penis.

Procedure:

1. Using references indicated above examine the microscopic sections of the testes. Find and identify the following structures:

Primary and secondary spermatocytes
Endocrine cells
Spermatozoa
Interstitial cells of Leydig
Sertoli cells
Lumen

2. Label Figure 92 with the above terms.

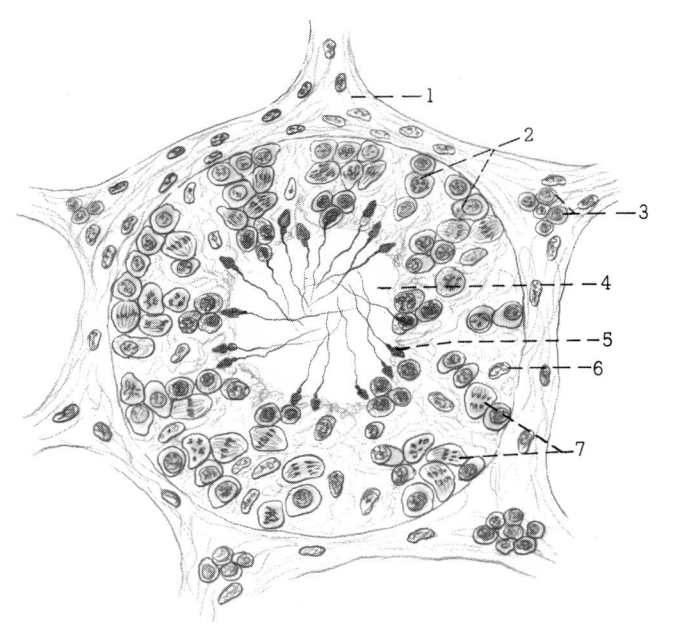

Figure 92. Spermatogenesis.

3. Using the terms listed below label Figure 93 of a section of the male testis. Also indicate with arrows the direction of sperm from the time of its formation until it is ready to leave the body:

Vas deferens	Lobe of testis
Rete testis	Septum of testis
Body of epididymis	Tunica vaginalis
Seminiferous tubule	Tail of epididymis
Vasa efferentia	

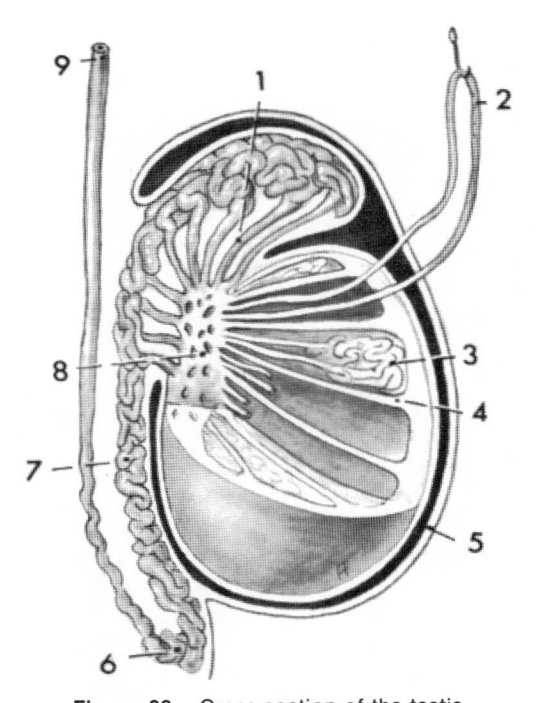

Figure 93. Cross section of the testis.

4. Examine cross section of the human penis; identify the following structures; label Fig. 94.

Corpus cavernosum   Superficial dorsal vein
Corpus spongiosum   Deep dorsal vein
Penile urethra   Dorsal artery

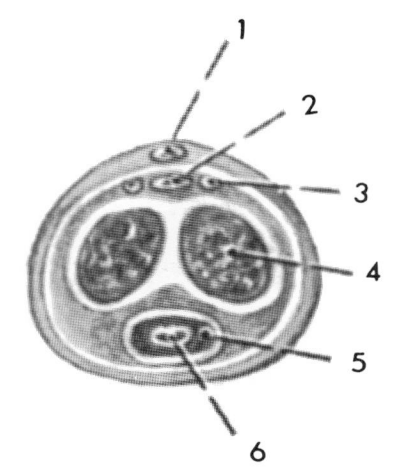

Figure 94. Cross section of the penis.

EXPERIMENT C: Female Reproductive System

References:

J & F, Ch. 17; appropriate chapters in Greisheimer, Kimber et al., Anthony, Reith et al., King & Showers, Dienhart, Chaffee & Greisheimer.

Materials:

1. Embalmed female cat or other mammal (demonstration)
2. Model of female pelvis
3. Preserved and fresh uterus and ovaries when available (demonstration)

Objective: To observe the characteristics of the female reproductive system.

Procedure:

1. Using the references indicated above, examine model of female pelvis, dissecting embalmed female cat, preserved and fresh uterus and ovaries, and identify the following structures:

Vagina	Uterine tube	Fundus of uterus
Anus	Ovary	Infundibulum
Rectum	Fimbria	External os
Recto-uterine pouch	Round ligament	Bartholin's glands
Fourchet	Cervix	Uterine tube
Hymen	Bladder	Uterine cavity
Vaginal orifice	Symphysis pubis	Anal canal
Urethral meatus	Clitoris	Uterus
Prepuce of clitoris	Labium minus	
Mons pubis	Labium majus	
	Urethra	

2. Label Figures 95 to 97 with the above terms.

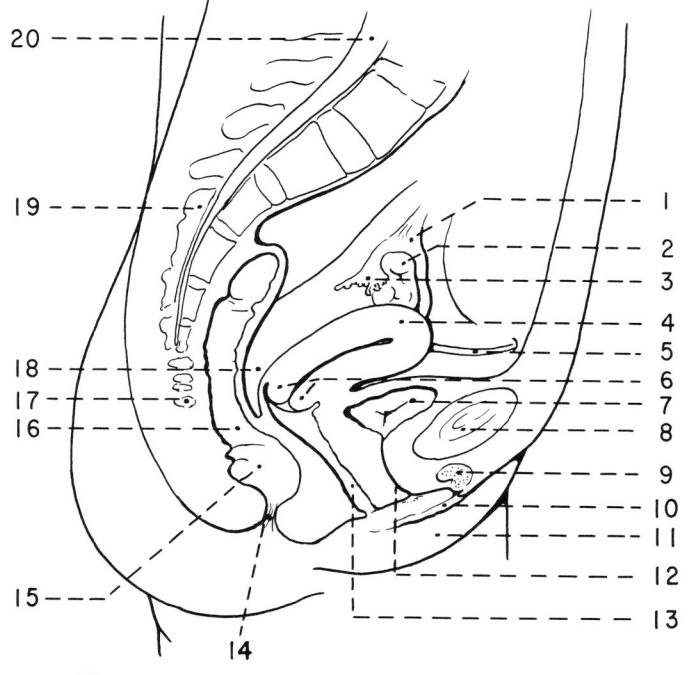

Figure 95. Midsagittal section of the female pelvis.

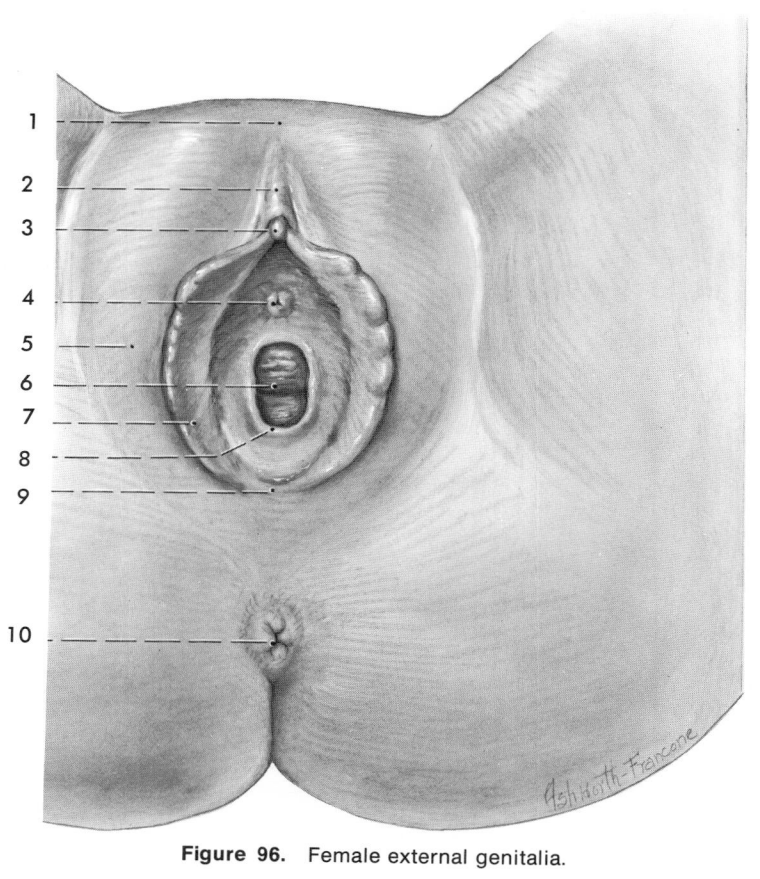

Figure 96. Female external genitalia.

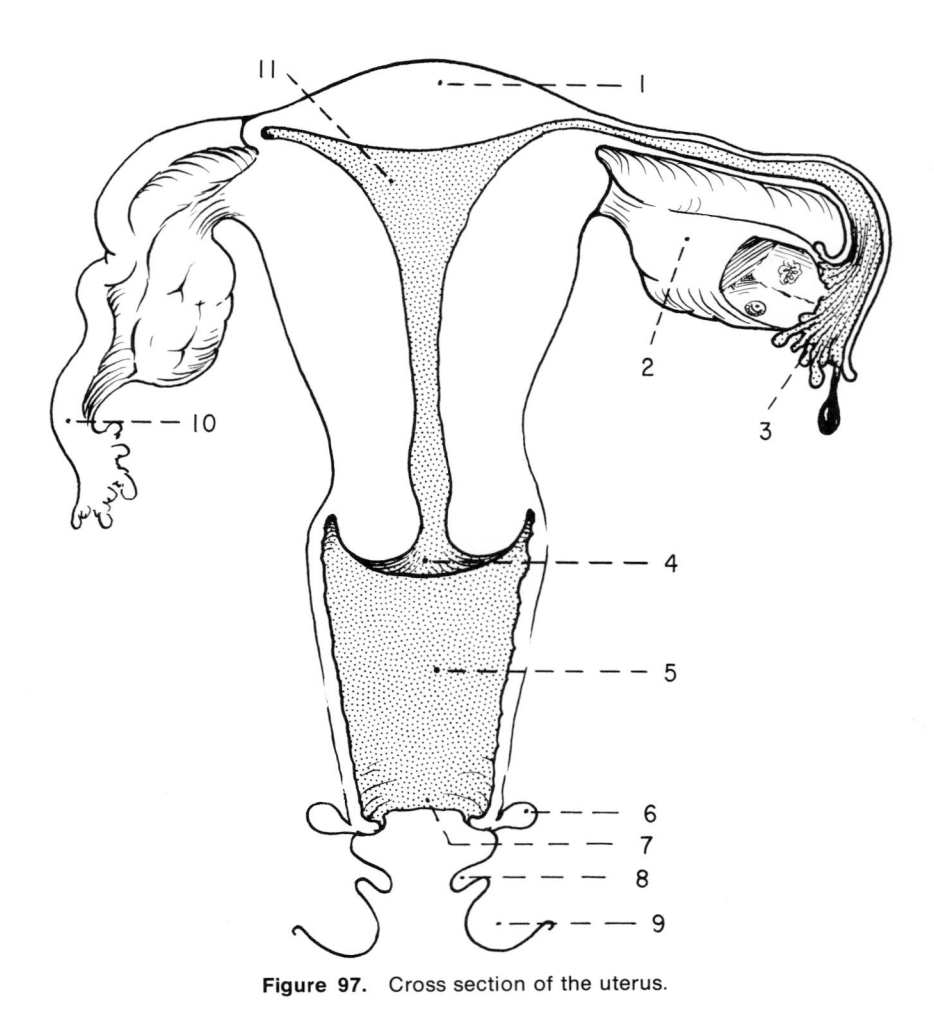

Figure 97. Cross section of the uterus.

EXPERIMENT D: Histology of the Ovary, Uterus, and Vagina

References:

J & F, Ch. 17; appropriate chapters in Greisheimer, Kimber et al., Anthony, Guyton, Reith et al., King & Showers, Dienhart, Chaffee & Greisheimer, Ham & Leeson.

Materials:

1. Histologic sections of ovarian, uterine, vaginal tissues
2. Microscope

Objective: To demonstrate the major microscopic structural characteristics of the ovary.

Procedure:

1. Using the references indicated above, examine cross sections of ovarian tissue, and identify the following structures:

    Ovum   Connective tissue of ovary

    Corpus luteum   Primary follice (single layer)

    Corpus albicans   Mature follicle (Graafian follicle)

    Blood vessels

2. Label Figure 98 with the above terms.

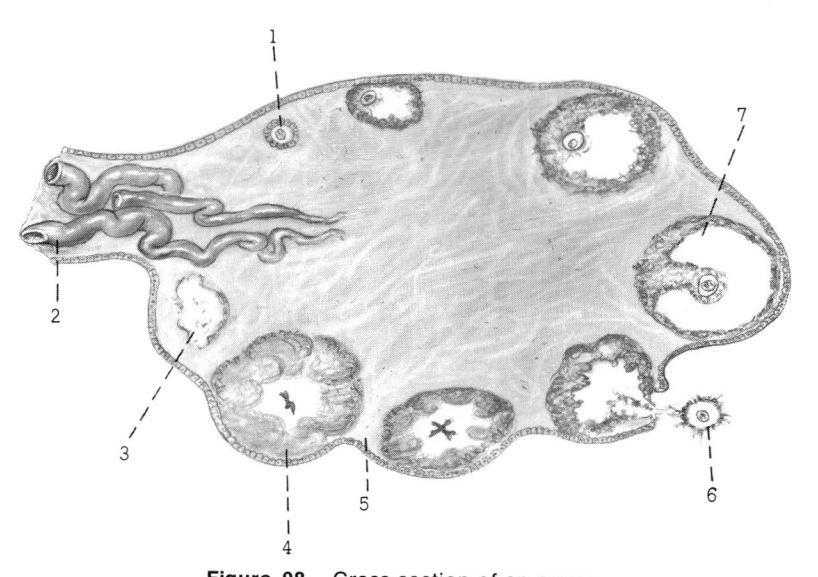

Figure 98. Cross section of an ovary.

3. Using the references indicated above, examine sections of uterine and vaginal tissue. Identify the following:

       Uterus:
         Serosa
         Myometrium
         Endometrium
       Vagina:
         Mucous Membrane (stratified squamous)
         Submucosa
         Muscle layer

EXPERIMENT E: Mammary Glands (Optional)

References:

J & F, Ch. 17; appropriate chapters in Greisheimer, Kimber et al., Anthony, Reith et al., King & Showers, Dienhart, Chaffee & Greisheimer, Ham & Leeson.

Materials:

Sections of nipple and mammary tissue (lactating and non-lactating)

Procedure:

1. Using the references indicated above examine sections of the mammary gland, nipple, and mammary tissue. Identify the following:

> Nipple:
>> Epidermis
>> Lactiferous duct
>> Lactiferous sinus
>> Smooth muscle
> Mammary tissue—lactating:
>> Lactiferous ducts and alveoli
>> Fat lobules
> Mammary tissue—non-lactating:
>> Lactiferous ducts
> Interlobular connective tissue

2. Label Figure 99 with the following:

> Lactiferous sinus   Lobule of gland tissue
> Areolar glands   Nipple
> Areola   Lactiferous duct

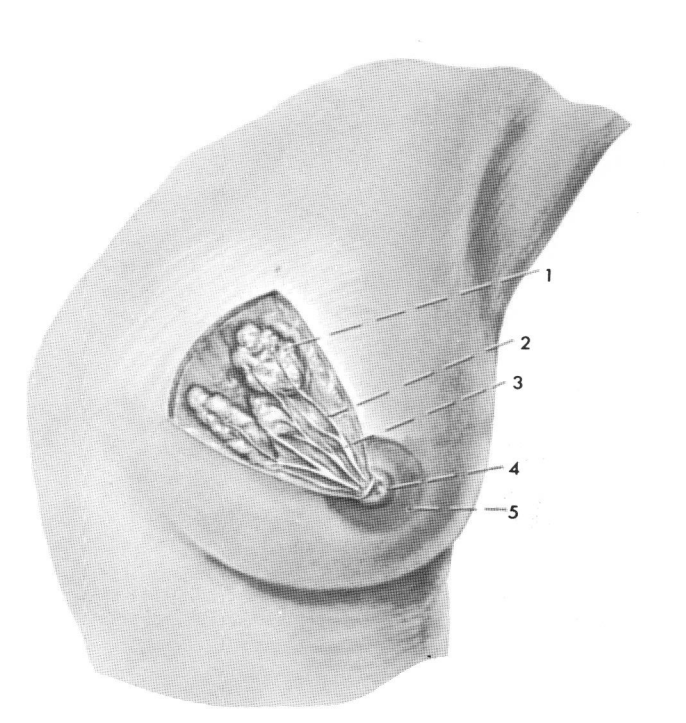

Figure 99.

PHYSIOLOGY OF THE REPRODUCTIVE SYSTEM

EXPERIMENT F: Gametogenesis (Meiosis—Demonstration)

References:

J & F, Ch. 17; appropriate chapters in Greisheimer, Kimber et al., Guyton, Reith et al., King & Showers, Dienhart, Chaffee & Greisheimer, Ham & Leeson.

Materials:

Histologic sections of salamander testes

Objective: To observe meiosis in reproductive tissue.

Procedure:

1. Using references indicated above examine slides of spermatogenesis. Find the following stages:

> Spermatogonia
> Primary spermatocytes
> Metaphase of first maturation division
> Secondary spermatocytes
> Metaphase of second maturation division
> Spermatids
> Spermatozoa

2. Label Figure 100 with the following.

> Spermatogonium   Primary oocyte
> Primary spermatocyte   First polar body
> Secondary spermatocyte   Secondary oocyte
> Spermatids   Second polar body
> Spermatozoa   Mature ovum
> Oogonium

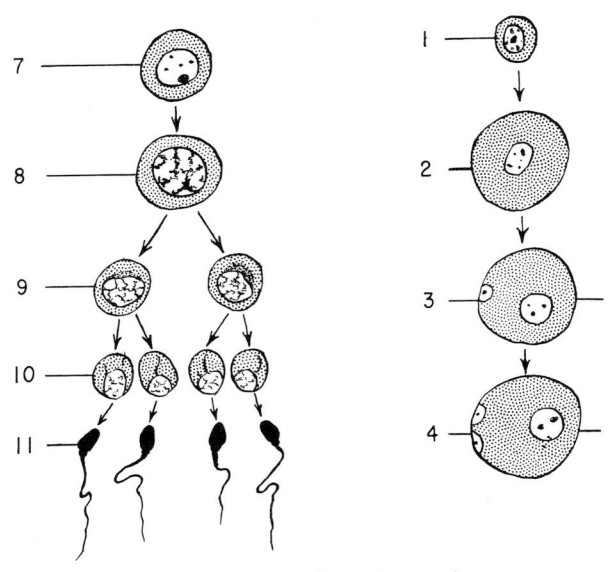

Figure 100. Gametogenesis.

EXPERIMENT G: Menstrual Cycle (Optional)

References:

J & F, Ch. 17; appropriate chapters in Greisheimer, Kimber et al., Anthony, Guyton, Reith et al., King & Showers, Dienhart, Chaffee & Greisheimer, Ham & Leeson.

Procedure:

1. Using references indicated above examine charts and illustrations of the menstrual cycle.

    a. Discuss briefly the three phases of the menstrual cycle:

_____

_____

_____

    b. What is the most favorable period during the menstrual cycle for fertilization? _____

_____

EXPERIMENT H: Biologic Tests for Pregnancy

References:

Hon, E. H.: A Manual of Pregnancy Testing. Boston, Little Brown, 1961.

Taylor, E. S.: Beck's Obstetrical Practice. The Williams and Wilkins Co., Balt., 1966, Ch. 8.

Eastman, N. J., and Hellman, L. M.: Obstetrics. Appleton-Century-Crofts, N. Y., 1966, Ch. 9.

Materials:

1. Recently voided first morning urine specimen of suspected pregnant female

2. Male frog

3. Syringe

4. HCG Test Kit (see appendix)

Objective: To test for pregnancy.

Procedure:

1. Use a recently voided first morning urine sample. Keep the urine refrigerated when not in use. Filter the urine if it is cloudy. Allow specimen to reach room temperature before injecting.

2. Place a male frog in a clean, dry jar. Inject 5 cc. of the urine to be tested into the anterior or abdominal lymph sac and return the frog to the jar. To inject the urine into the lymph sac force the frog's mouth open with the point of the syringe needle and pass the needle into the mouth, avoiding the tongue. Direct the needle point downward toward the floor of the mouth. With a little pressure the needle will pierce and enter the lymph sac. As it is pushed down the sac, the point will be seen beneath the skin of the abdominal wall. Now inject the urine into the sac.

After 1 hour, if the frog has voided, pipette the urine into a glass slide and examine microscopically for spermatozoa. If the frog has not voided, grasping it while it is in the jar will usually induce voiding. If the 1-hour urine does not contain spermatozoa, repeat the procedure at 2 hours.

3. The presence of spermatozoa is a positive test for pregnancy and indicates the presence of gonadotropin in the injected urine. Very early in pregnancy gonadotropic substances are secreted by the trophoblast and may be found in the urine. This chorionic gonadotropin is capable of stimulating the gonads of lower animals.

4. Another rapid pregnancy test, called the HCG test (Hyland Laboratories) is done on a glass slide and takes only a few minutes. A suspension of latex particles coated with human chorionic gonadotropin (HCG), when combined with rabbit anti-HCG serum, causes the latex particles to agglutinate. If the latex particles are first brought together with pregnancy urine there is no agglutination. If no agglutination occurs, then the test is positive for pregnancy.

EMBRYOLOGY

EXPERIMENT I: Pregnant Uterus and Embryological Development

References:
   J & F, Ch. 17; appropriate chapters in Greisheimer, Kimber et al.,
Anthony, Guyton, King & Showers, Chaffee & Greisheimer.
Materials:
   1. Preserved human embryos at different stages of development when
available (demonstration).
   2. Fertile chicken eggs showing various stages of embryological
development.
   3. Models of human embryos at different stages of development.
Objective: To show the major characteristics of embryological development.
Procedure:
   1. Obtain fertile chicken eggs showing various stages of developing
embryos from a local poultry hatcher. Each student should open one egg by
carefully removing a portion of the shell above the embryo with sharp pointed
forceps (try not to damage the underlying embryo). Observe the other developing chicken embryos in the classroom. Write a brief description of some of the
major embryological characteristics you have observed in the chick embryos.
   2. Using references indicated above examine models and preserved
human embryos. Observe what your instructor thinks is important.
   3. Using references indicated above examine illustrations of a pregnant
uterus; then label Figure 101 with the following terms:

Umbilical cord	Capsularis vera and parietalis vera
Placenta	Decidua basalis
Amnion	Uterine artery
Chorion	Uterine vein
Vagina	Ovary
Embryo (fetus)	Uterine tube (fallopian tube)
Fimbria	Ampulla
Broad ligament	Isthmus
External and internal os	Fornix of vagina

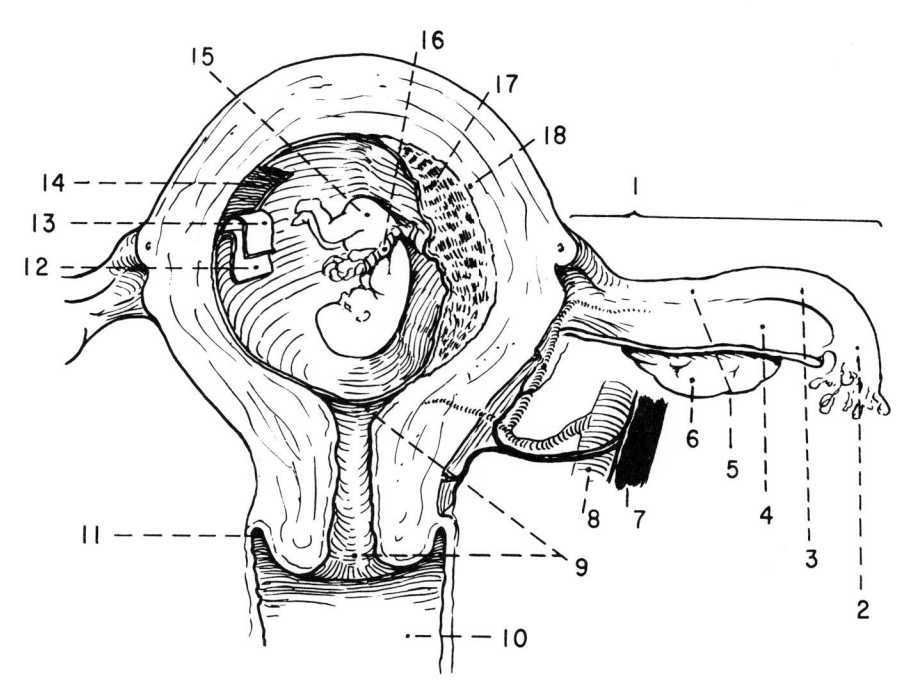

Figure 101. Frontal section of a pregnant uterus.

PRACTICAL EXERCISES

ANATOMY AND PHYSIOLOGY QUESTIONS

　　1. At what age do the reproductive organs of the male become functionally mature? _____ Of the female? _____

　　2. List the accessory male reproductive glands. What is the function of each? _____

_____

_____

_____

　　3. What is the spermatic cord? _____

_____

_____

_____

　　4. Define spermatogenesis: _____

_____

_____

_____

　　5. Give name and function of the hormones produced by the testes: _____

_____

_____

_____

　　6. Define menopause: _____

_____

_____

_____

　　7. Name two hormones produced by the ovary: _____

　　8. Which hormones do the following?
　　　　a. Stimulates ovarian follicle to start forming: _____
　　　　b. Stimulates ovarian follicle to secrete: _____
　　　　c. Causes follicle to ovulate: _____
　　　　d. Causes corpus luteum to form: _____
　　　　e. Stimulates corpus luteum to secrete: _____
　　　　f. Stimulates proliferation of the endometrium: _____
　　　　g. Inhibits the secretion of follicle-secreting hormone: _____
　　　　h. Stimulates secretion of luteinizing hormone: _____
　　　　i. Stimulates secretory changes in the endometrium: _____
　　9. Define lactation: _____

_____

What causes lactation? _____

10. Discuss the importance of the sucking stimulus after birth: _____

_____

_____

_____

CLINICAL QUESTIONS

1. Which of the following procedures would cause sterility? State your reasons briefly:

a. Orchiectomy (removal of testes): _____

_____

b. Prostatectomy: _____

_____

c. Severing of both seminal ducts: _____

_____

2. How does enlargement of the prostate gland restrict the normal flow of urine from the bladder? _____

_____

_____

_____

3. How would overexposure of the gonads to x-rays or other radiation reduce normal sex cell production? _____

_____

_____

_____

4. Why would a tubal pregnancy fail to reach full term? _____

_____

_____

_____

5. Briefly define the following terms:

a. Mastectomy: _____

_____

b. Salpingitis: _____

_____

c. Ectopic pregnancy: _____

_____

d. Vaginal hysterectomy: _____

_____

e. Cervicitis: _____

_____

    f. Rectocele: _____

_____

    g. Circumcision: _____

_____

    h. Amenorrhea: _____

_____

    i. D & C (Dilation and Curettage): _____

_____

APPENDIX

CONVERSION TABLES
(Comparison of metric with English measures)

A. **Length:**

1 kilometer = 100 meters = 0.62 mile

1 meter = 100 centimeters = 1000 millimeters (mm.) = 39.37 inches = 1.09 yards

1 millimeter = 1/25 inch (approximately)

1 micron (1μ) = 1 micromillimeter = 1/1000 millimeter = 1/25,000 inch

1 inch = 2.5 cm. (approximately)

1 mile = 1.6 kilometers

B. **Volume**

1 liter = $\begin{cases} 1000 \text{ milliliters (ml.)} \\ 1000 \text{ cubic centimeters (cc.)} \end{cases}$ = $\begin{cases} 0.9 \text{ dry quart} \\ 1.05 \text{ liquid quarts} \end{cases}$ = $\begin{cases} 33.8 \text{ fluid} \\ \text{ounces} \end{cases}$

1 dry quart = 1.1 liter

1 liquid quart = 0.905 liter (L.) = 905 ml.

1 fluid ounce (oz.) = 28.35 ml.

1 cubic inch = 16.38 ml. or cubic centimeters

1 pint = 473.2 ml.

C. **Weight:**

1 gram (gm.) = 1000 milligrams (mg.) = 15.43 grains (gr.)

1 kilogram (kg.) = 1000 grams (gm.) = 2.2 pounds or 35.27 ounces

1 pound = 453.6 gm. (approximately)

1 ounce = 28.35 gm.

1 milligram = 1000 μg. of gammas

1 microgram (1 μg., gamma) = 0.001 mg. = 1/28,000 ounce

D. Thermometric conversion factors:

To convert centigrade degrees into Fahrenheit degrees multiply centigrade figure by $9/5$ and add 32 to the result.
To convert Fahrenheit into centigrade degrees subtract 32 from the Fahrenheit number and multiply the difference by $5/9$.

E. Approximate measures:

1 drop = 1/15 ml.

1 teaspoonful = 4 ml.

1 tablespoonful = 15 ml.

1 teacupful = 120 ml.

1 tumblerful = 240 ml.

1 glass = 250 ml.

SOLUTIONS

Anticoagulants for blood:

For each 10 ml. of blood use: 1.20 mg. of sodium oxalate *or* 2.200 mg. of sodium citrate.

Ringer's solution — buffered (frogs):

NaCl	6.50 gm.
KCl	0.14 gm.
$CaCl_2 \cdot H_2O$	0.12 gm.
NaH_2PO_4	0.01 gm.
$NaHCO_3$	0.20 gm.
Distilled water to make	1 liter

Ringer's solution (mammalian):

NaCl	9.00 gm.
KCl	0.42 gm.
$CaCl_2 \cdot H_2O$	0.24 gm.
$NaHCO_3$	0.20 gm.
Distilled water to make	1 liter

Normal saline solution for cold-blooded animals:

0.7% NaCl in distilled water—7 gm. NaCl/liter H_2O

Normal saline solution for warm-blooded animals:

0.9% NaCl in distilled water—9 gm. NaCl/liter H_2O

Lugol's iodine solution:

Iodine crystals	1 gm.
Iodide of potassium	2 gm.
Distilled water	300 ml.

Benedict's solution:

Copper sulfate (pure crystalline $CuSO_4 \cdot H_2O$)	17.3 gm.
Sodium citrate	173 gm.
Sodium carbonate (anhydrous)	100 gm.
Distilled water to make	1 liter

Methylene blue solution:

10 mg. methylene blue

water q.s. 100 ml.

Wright's stain and Wright's stain buffer:

May be obtained in ready to use solutions from hospital and laboratory supply houses.

5% adrenalin and acetylcholine solution:

> Add 0.5 gm. acetylcholine chloride to 10 ml. distilled H_2O
> Add 0.5 gm. adrenalin to 10 ml. distilled H_2O

1:1000 adrenalin and acetylcholine solutions:

Available from any drug supply house.

Locke's solution (mammalian):

NaCl	0.900 gm.
KCl	0.042 gm.
$CaCl_2$	0.024 gm.
$NaHCO_3$	0.02 gm.
glucose	0.10 to 0.25 gm.

Distilled water to make 100 ml.

REFERENCES

Allen, R. M.: The Microscope. D. Van Nostrand Co., Inc., New York, 1940.

Anthony, C. P.: Textbook of Anatomy and Physiology. The C. V. Mosby Co., St. Louis, 1967.

Chaffee, E. E., and Greisheimer, E. M.: Basic Physiology and Anatomy. J. B. Lippincott Co., Philaphia, 1964.

Decoursey, R. M.: The Human Organism. McGraw-Hill Book Co., New York, 1961.

Dienhart, C. M.: Basic Human Anatomy and Physiology. W. B. Saunders Co., Philadelphia, 1967.

Gage, S. H.: The Microscope. The Comstock Publishing Co., Ithaca, New York, 1936.

Greisheimer, E. M.: Physiology and Anatomy. J. B. Lippincott Co., Philadelphia, 1963.

Guyton, A. C.: Textbook of Medical Physiology. W. B. Saunders Co., Philadelphia, 1967.

Hamm, A. W., and Leeson, T. S.: Histology, J. B. Lippincott Co., Philadelphia, 1961.

Jacob, S. W., and Francone, C. A.: Structure and Function in Man. W. B. Saunders Co., Philadelphia, 1970.

Kimber, D. C., Gray, C. E., Stackpole, C. E., and Leavell, L. C.: Anatomy and Physiology. The Macmillan Co., New York, 1961.

King, B. G., and Showers, M. J.: Human Anatomy and Physiology. W. B. Saunders Co., Philadelphia, 1969.

Needham, G. H.: Practical Use of the Microscope. Charles C Thomas, Springfield, Illinois, 1958.

Reith, E. J., Breidenbach, B. and Lorenc, M.: Anatomy and Physiology, McGraw-Hill Book Co., New York, 1964.

Swanson, C. P.: The Cell. Prentice Hall, Englewood Cliffs, New Jersey, 1964.

Animal Dissection Manuals

Laboratory Anatomy of the Cat. Ernest S. Booth, Wm. C. Brown Co., Inc., Dubuque, Iowa.

Representative Chordates (emphasis on the cat). Charles K. Weichert, McGraw-Hill Book Co., Inc.

Functional Anatomy of the Mammal (a guide to the dissection of the cat and an introduction to the structural and functional relationship between the cat and man). W. James Leach, McGraw-Hill Co., Inc.

Atlas of Cat Anatomy. David B. Horsburgh, James P. Heath, Stanford University Press, Stanford, California.

Laboratory Anatomy of the Fetal Pig. Theron O. Odlang, Wm. C. Brown Co. Inc., Dubuque, Iowa.

The Fetal Pig — A Photographic Study. W. L. Evans, Addison E. Lee, George Tatum, Holt, Rinehart and Winston.

Guide to the Dissection of the Dog. Malcolm E. Miller, Edwards Brothers, Inc.

Topographical Anatomy of the Dog. O. Charnock Bradley, Revised by Tom Grahame, The Macmillan Co.

Anatomy of the Domestic Animals (pig, dog, chicken). Septimus Sisson, Revised by James Daniels, Grossman, W. B. Saunders Co.

The Rat[*] (with notes on the mouse).

Laboratory Anatomy of the White Rat. Robert B. Chiasson, Wm. C. Brown Co. Inc., Dubuque, Iowa.

The Frog.[*]

Laboratory Anatomy of the Frog. Raymond A. Underhill, Wm. C. Brown Co. Inc., Dubuque, Iowa.

Laboratory Anatomy of the Pigeon. Robert B. Chiasson, Wm. C. Brown Co. Inc., Dubuque, Iowa.

The Rabbit.[*]

Bensley's Practical Anatomy of the Rabbit. B. A. Bensley, Revised by E. Horne, Craigie, The Blackiston Co., Philadelphia.

A *Laboratory Guide to the Anatomy of the Rabbit.* E. Horne, Craigie, Revised Edition, University of Toronto Press, Toronto.

---

[*]Dissection Guides (inexpensive yet very good), H.G.Q. Rowett.